BRIDGES

by the author of

MAN BEFORE ADAM

NIELS BOHR: THE MAN WHO MAPPED THE ATOM

BRIDGES

Robert Silverberg

MACRAE SMITH COMPANY
PHILADELPHIA

The graceful MACKINAC BRIDGE,
spanning the Straits of Mackinac in Michigan,
is shown in the title page illustration.

ACKNOWLEDGMENTS

The author wishes to thank the Michigan Tourist Council
for permission to use the photographs on the title page and
page 152, the Bettman Archive for those on pages 19, 20, 63,
70, 93; the French Government Tourist Office for pages 37,
46, 50; the Italian State Tourist Office for pages 48, 49, 53;
the New York City Department of Public Works for pages
88, 97; the Pennsylvania Railroad Company for page 102;
the Canadian Government Travel Bureau for page 99; the
State of California Department of Public Works, Division of
Highways for pages 129, 131; the Delaware River Port
Authority and "Skyphotos, Phila." for page 122 (bottom);
the Redwood Empire Association for pages 133, 136; the
Port of New York Authority for pages 103, 114, 116; the
Swedish Information Service for page 106; the Triborough
Bridge and Tunnel Authority for pages 105, 119, 120, 122,
163, 166, 168, 169; the Chesapeake Bay Bridge Tunnel for
pages 155, 158, 159; and World Wide Photos for page 145.

CONTENTS

1:

A LOG AND A STREAM   13

    History's First Bridges   21

    Pontoon Bridges   24

2:

THE ROMANS SHOW THE WORLD HOW   27

    Roman Engineering Techniques   29

    Some Famous Roman Bridges   33

3:

BRIDGES OF THE MIDDLE AGES   39

    London Bridge   40

    The Pont d'Avignon   44

    The Late Middle Ages   47

4:

THE IRON AGE   55

    Iron Bridges   56

    Suspension Bridges   58

    Truss Bridges   61

    Railroad Bridges   64

5:

CAPTAIN EADS BUILDS A BRIDGE   67

    Bridging the Mississippi in St. Louis   67

6:

ROEBLING & SON, ENGINEERS   79

    Niagara Bridge   81

    Brooklyn Bridge   84

7:

NEW BRIDGES FOR A NEW CENTURY   91

    Cantilever Bridges   91

    Steel Arch Bridges   100

    Reinforced Concrete Bridges   105

8:

SPANNING THE HUDSON   109

    The George Washington Bridge   113

9:

A BRIDGE FOR THE GOLDEN GATE   125

   San Francisco-Oakland Bay Bridge   127

   Golden Gate Bridge   132

10:

THE DEATH OF ''GALLOPING GERTIE''   139

   Tacoma-Narrows Bridge   140

11:

AN ERA OF GIANT BRIDGES   151

   The Mackinac Straits Bridge   151

   The Chesapeake Bay Bridge-Tunnel   154

   The Varrazano-Narrows Bridge   161

12:

BRIDGES OF TOMORROW   171

   The Long Island Sound Bridge   173

   The Humber River Bridge   173

   The Tokyo Bay Bridge   174

   The Messina Straits Bridge   174

BIBLIOGRAPHY   177

INDEX   179

BRIDGES

1:

A Log And A Stream

SOME TIME IN THE DISTANT PAST, A MAN LOWERED A LOG ACROSS A stream, and built humanity's first bridge. We do not know where or when it happened. As that pioneer of engineers laid his slab of wood into place, he began a chain of progress that, reaching into our own times, has culminated in the majestic, gleaming grandeur of our great bridges.

The bridge-building idea does not go back to the very dawn of humanity. Before a man goes to the trouble of constructing a bridge, he must have some pressing reason for wanting to get to the other side of the stream that blocks him. The most primitive men, naked and nomadic, with no possessions other than their stone handaxes or knives, did not *need* bridges. If, in their wanderings, they came to a stream that lay in their path, they would simply have waded across, or perhaps have crossed by swimming. If the water were too broad and deep, they would merely wander off in another direction, giving up the attempt to cross entirely.

The building of bridges implies a fair degree of civilization and intelligence. A bridge-builder must have the need to get across water (to the fertile fields beyond, perhaps) and he must want to cross dry-shod (to protect his clothing and possessions). Bridge-building springs from the desire to maintain and extend an orderly, settled way of life, with ready communication from place to place. Mankind did not develop those needs until quite recently, relatively speaking. So, although man has inhabited the Earth for hundreds of thousands of years, the concept of the bridge may be no more than ten thousand years old.

Probably the first bridge-builders arrived at the idea through observing the accidental bridges about them. A tree trunk may have fallen happily over a stream from bank to bank. Looking at it, some genius of 8000 B.C. may have thought, "Suppose I chop down a tree, and put it across the stream in a different place——"

Other clues suggested different types of bridges. In many parts of the world, natural bridges of stone have been formed, where the action of water has worn away rock until only an arch is left, high above the riverbed. The American Southwest has a number of spectacular natural bridges. There is a famous one in Virginia which Thomas Jefferson once studied. A particularly fine natural bridge is the Pont d'Arc, in France, whose 194-foot span rises 111 feet over the river that chiseled it. Men who grew up in the shadow of such a wonder of nature must eventually have thought of imitating it by placing a flat slab of rock across a stream, thus creating the basic form of the stone bridge.

In the tropical parts of the world, creeping vines of great strength and thickness hang from tree to tree. How many thousands of years had to pass before some jungle-dweller, pondering those long, thick, ropelike vines, got the idea of tying them between two trees that spanned an abyss? The idea was born, eventually— and with it, yet another type of bridge.

Bridge of wood, bridge of stone, bridge of vines—man's restless mind conceived them all, over thousands of years. Most likely they were invented again and again, in many parts of the world at different times, since the spread of ideas was painfully slow in those remote days. All three types of bridges have their descendants today, though the materials are different. Time's evolution has transformed the flimsy, swaying vine-bridge of the tropics into the steely splendor of the modern suspension bridge. The log across the stream has become the beam, or girder, bridge. The bridge of several braced stone slabs has developed into the arch bridge, which the Romans fashioned with such artful cunning. How these changes came about is something we will see, as we go forward in time on the track of yesterday's engineers.

The wooden bridge was probably the earliest bridge of the northern lands, where there were no tropical vines to be used. A log laid across a narrow stream sufficed at first. Fresh water was necessary to the life of any community, and settlements sprang up at places where streams flowed and where the source of the water, thanks to the presence of the bridge, did not form any barrier to travel.

A bridge consisting of a log or a flat slab of stone is known as a *simple beam bridge*. It is the most basic of bridges. Its weight descends vertically, at right angles to the ground, along its whole length.

Engineers sometimes call simple beam bridges made of logs or tree trunks *clam bridges,* from an Anglo-Saxon word meaning "twig" or "stick." A beam bridge made of a single flat slab of stone is known technically as a *clapper bridge,* from another Anglo-Saxon word meaning "stepping-stone." In Great Britain the remains of clapper bridges more than two thousand years old have been discovered by archaeologists.

The builders of these simple bridges soon ran into serious engineering problems. What does one do when the stream to be bridged is wider than the length of any available tree trunk? The solution seems simple to us, but it may have been slow in coming to our far-removed ancestors.

What they did—eventually—was to build supports, or *piers,* at shallow points in the stream. Every 20 or 30 feet they set up a crude structure made of piled boughs and branches, or perhaps threw big stones into the water until the heap reached the surface. Then tree trunks could be placed from one pier to the next, so that the bridge spanned the stream from bank to bank. In this way, a stream several hundred feet wide could be bridged, employing a great many short spans, provided only that there were enough shallow places where piers could be erected in the bed of the stream.

Many modern bridges still follow this principle. A flat road-bed—made of steel or concrete now, of course, not wood—crosses the stream or river, supported by piers in several places. These are known as *continuous span girder bridges,* and they consist, basically, of several single span bridges joined end to end. A bridge of this type built across the River Sava in Yugoslavia in 1956 has a total span of 856 feet. How it would have astonished the builders of those early bridges across 20-foot brooks!

In time, stone slabs and not wooden logs became the chief material for prehistoric simple beam bridges. Stone is more durable than wood; but it created a different kind of engineering difficulty for the ancient bridge-builders. Stone is heavy and is not really a good bridge-building material because of its low tensile strength. That is, stone has little flexibility under stress. It does not give or bend; it simply snaps. A sudden blow from above—a falling boulder, even a toppling tree—can shatter a slab of stone that is stretched across two supports. A long beam of stone may even be so brittle that it collapses under its own weight when placed on supports. The tension on the middle of the beam is great enough to exert a downward pull that breaks the beam in two.

The clapper-type bridge, consisting of flat slabs of stone lying on end-supports, thus had serious limitations. It could not support great weight or sudden increase in tension, and was apt to collapse unexpectedly from its own massiveness. The longer the slab, the more likely it was to collapse. Eventually a refinement of the clapper bridge took care of this problem, and produced the ancestor of the *arch bridge.*

By our standards, these early arch bridges were crude and awkward things. They consisted of slabs of stone raised at a 45-degree angle from the horizontal, and roughly bevelled so that they leaned against each other at their upraised ends. The weight of the bridge no longer dropped vertically. Now, the two slabs forming the sections of such a bridge thrust against each other, and also against the support, or *abutment,* at each outer end of the bridge. The stress on any given part of the bridge was thus reduced.

Although such bridges looked clumsy, and *were* clumsy, they represented a tremendously sophisticated approach to bridge-building, compared with what had gone before. An important engineering problem in bridge design has always been weight distribution: how to arrange things so that the bridge can stand up under its own weight and the weight of the load it is expected to carry. This involves coping with the forces of *tension* and *compression*. Tension is the force that pulls or tries to stretch; compression is the force that squeezes together or tries to shorten.

In a simple beam bridge, compression is no major problem, for a hard substance such as stone can resist a great deal of compression before it gives way. But the vertical pull of gravity creates a good deal of tension. The leaning-slab stone bridge, by relieving this vertical weight pull and thrusting outwards, was a considerable advance over the simple beam. Using such a bridge, though, was tricky and uncomfortable, for the roadbed rose steeply on one side and descended just as steeply on the other.

It took the Romans to perfect this sort of bridge by going the final step to the true arch. Over a period of centuries, as we will shortly see, the Romans learned how to build semicircular arches that were so well designed that many of them still stand after twenty centuries.

The bridge of vines was the first *suspension bridge.* As the name implies, such a bridge is suspended, dangling freely from cables anchored at either end. The suspension bridge is in a state of tension, always trying to pull inward, while the two anchoring towers everlastingly resist. The interplay of these two pulls keeps the bridge in place over the abyss it spans.

Today's suspension bridges—such as the Brooklyn Bridge, the George Washington Bridge, and the Golden Gate Bridge—are anchored by mighty columns of concrete and steel. The earliest types of suspension bridges were by no means as substantial. Fashioned from vines or ropes, they were anchored by tying them to rock outcroppings or sturdy trees at either side of a gorge. In many parts of the world, vine or rope suspension bridges are still in use—and many a traveler has walked over one with his fingers crossed and a prayer on his lips!

In western China, suspension bridges have for thousands of years been made of two-inch-thick rope of plaited bamboo. The most basic of these rope bridges is constructed simply of two ropes hung across a river, one above the other. The traveler stands on the lower rope, gripping the upper one and trying to keep his balance. It is not a pleasant way to cross a river—particularly when the lower rope swings one way and the upper one swings the other way.

It is also not a very useful way to span a river, since no heavy burdens can be carried across such a bridge, only packs strapped to the back. A more effective Chinese and Indian rope bridge is the hammock type, with a woven bottom slung between two suspended cables laid side by side. The decks of such bridges can support surprisingly heavy loads, and even laden mules can cross them. One outstanding bridge of this sort is at Kwan Hsien, China. It is 700 feet long, and consists of five spans dangling from one pier to the next. The largest of these spans is 200 feet long. At each end of every span is a capstan arrangement, enabling the bridge-keepers to tighten the span when the cables begin to grow slack from wear.

Another variety, found in Tibet and parts of China, makes use of a movable seat slung under a suspended rope. The traveler seats himself and swings out over the gorge. To make this primitive species of cable car move swiftly and smoothly, the natives frequently grease the rope with butter. It makes for a quick ride but never a relaxing one.

Some ideas are so powerful that they crop up repeatedly all over the world, independently invented by many cultures. The buttered bridge is one of them. Although there was certainly no contact between Tibet and Peru, the Incas of Peru were using such bridges six hundred years ago. An 18th-century Spanish visitor to Peru, Don Antonio de Ulloa, set down this description of the *tarabita*, or Inca bridge:

"The *tarabita* is only a single rope made of *bejuco,* or thongs of ox hide . . . . This rope is fastened on each bank to strong posts. On one side is a kind of wheel, or winch, to straighten or slacken the *tarabita* to the degree required. From the *tarabita* hangs a leathern hammock capable of holding a man."

It may seem impossible that there could be any relationship

Native woven bridge in the Cameroons, West Africa.

Cord bridge used in South America.

between these flimsy rope bridges and the Golden Gate Bridge. Yet the line of descent is a straight one. The bridge of the Orient and South America, with a roadbed hung suspended on cables, is, so far as the basic engineering principle goes, a direct ancestor of our grandest contemporary suspension bridges.

History's First Bridges

History begins in the Near East: in Mesopotamia, the Land of the Two Rivers, and in Egypt. In these lands, some six thousand years ago, mankind's first true civilizations developed. The Sumerians of Mesopotamia and the early Egyptians were the first peoples to have written records, the first to undertake large-scale engineering projects, and the first to develop elaborate systems of government. Not surprisingly, the earliest bridges that we know anything about were built by these two civilizations.

The oldest bridge on record was built in Egypt, about 3,000 B.C., by the Pharaoh Menes of the First Dynasty. Unfortunately, no information has come down to us about this bridge other than the mere fact of its existence. With Egyptian life centered about the Nile, and Egyptian towns scattered on both banks of the great river for hundreds of miles, a natural motive for bridge-building existed in the land of the Pharaohs.

The Sumerians of Mesopotamia had two important rivers in their country, the Tigris and the Euphrates. Archaeologists tell us that the Sumerians built many bridges between 3,000 and 2,000 B.C., and that these bridges were sometimes of wood, sometimes of brick. The Sumerians, who invented writing, the plow, and the sailboat, probably also gave the world the concept of the arch— and used it in their bridges.

The idea of the arch is vital to the history of bridge-building and of all other construction. An arch is simply a curved structure. The Sumerians made the great discovery—improved upon by the Romans thousands of years later—that if bricks or stones are carefully arranged on a centering of timber formed in a curve, they will remain in place even after the centering has been removed. "An arch never sleeps," one proverb has it. Just as a suspension bridge is in constant tension, forever pulling inward, an arch is in a constant state of compression, always thrusting outward. If properly constructed, an arch will hold together through the interaction of its components. Each stone or brick, pushing outward against its neighbors, serves to help support the whole, even without mortar to glue them together.

The oldest bridge about which we have any real detail was built in Mesopotamia, but it was not an arch bridge. It was erected at the city of Babylon, long after the Sumerians had vanished from the world scene. Writing about 425 B.C., the Greek historian Herodotus described this bridge, which he claimed was constructed by the (mythical) Queen Nitocris:

"She gave orders for the hewing of immense blocks of stone, and when they were ready and the basin was excavated, she turned the entire stream of the Euphrates into the cutting, and thus for a time, while the basin was filling, the natural channel of the river was left dry. [That is, the Queen built a temporary dam across the river to divert it from its natural bed.] Forthwith she set to work . . . and built, as near the middle of the town as possible, a stone bridge, the blocks whereof were bound together with iron and lead. In the daytime square wooden platforms were laid along from pier to pier, on which the inhabitants crossed the stream; but at night they were withdrawn, to prevent people passing from side to side in the dark to commit robberies. When the river had filled the cutting, and the bridge was finished, the Euphrates was turned back again into its ancient bed."

A later historian, Diodorus Siculus, who lived in the time of Julius Caesar, provides even more detail about this bridge at Babylon, which he thought was built by the (also mythical) Queen Semiramis:

"She then made a bridge over the narrowest part of the river, five furlongs [five-eighths of a mile] in length, laying the supports and pillars of the arches with great art and skill at the bottom of the water, twelve feet distant from each other. That the stones might be the more firmly joined, they were bound together with hooks of iron, and the joints filled up with melted lead. And before the pillars she made and placed defenses, with sharp pointed angles, to receive the water before it beat upon the flat sides of the pillars, which caused the course of the water to run round by degrees gently and moderately, as far as to the broad sides of the pillars, so that the sharp points of the angles cut the stream, and gave a check to its violence. . . . This bridge was floored with great joists and planks of cedar, cypress, and palm trees, and was thirty feet in breadth, and for art and curiosity, yielded to none of the works of Semiramis."

Because both Herodotus and Diodorus Siculus were fond of including fantastic fairy tales in their books of history, and because neither Queen Nitocris nor Queen Semiramis was an authentic historical personage, this bridge at Babylon was long regarded with suspicion. Today we know that it existed. At the beginning of this century, a team of German archaeologists excavated the buried, ruined city of Babylon, and actually found the ancient bridge.

It had really been built about 625 B.C., the archaeologists discovered, by Nabopolassar, father of King Nebuchadnezzar. The bridge crossed the Euphrates River at a point where the river was about a thousand yards wide. More than a hundred piers, made of stone joined by a form of cement, had been set in the riverbed 17 to 20 feet apart, and over them had been laid a roadway 30 feet wide, made of palm-tree beams. The sides of the piers were tapered, exactly as described by Diodorus Siculus, to reduce the impact of the current as it battered against them.

To the eyes of a modern engineer, Nabopolassar's bridge was not a very good one. As a continuous span bridge, it represented hardly any technical advance at all over the tree trunk laid across a stream. Because the numerous piers were so close together, the river water did not have a free flow under the bridge. This not only blocked navigation, by creating narrow slots through which all ships had to pass, but tended to cause flooding of the shore at times of high water. Furthermore, the narrowing of the flow path caused the water to surge more swiftly, setting up forces that would eventually help to undermine the piers. Unless a bridge is intended to serve also as a dam, the piers must be far apart, permitting the river to flow freely between them.

The flat, beam-type bridge cannot have widely spaced piers

because of its low tensile strength. The individual spans, with their tendency to collapse of their own weight, would not have sufficient support if the piers were too far apart. This sort of bridge *had* to have a pier every twenty feet. A Roman bridge-designer would have sneered at the Babylon bridge. An arch design should have been used.

We do not know why Nabopolassar's engineers preferred the beam construction. Certainly the Babylonians understood the use of the arch at that time, since archaeologists have discovered ancient buildings of the city that did employ arch construction. And the Sumerians had been building arch bridges in Mesopotamia thousands of years before Nabopolassar came to the Babylonian throne. Why such a faulty design, then?

We will never know. But, for all its weaknesses, the Babylonian bridge was a landmark in engineering history. It was the biggest bridge of its time, and it is the oldest bridge whose fragments still survive today.

Pontoon Bridges

Another type of bridge that has been in use in Mesopotamia (now Iraq) for thousands of years, since Sumerian times, is the bridge of boats. This is no more than a series of small vessels lashed together from one bank of a river to the other, with a roadbed laid above them. Such bridges are fragile, easily swept away in time of flood. But they have an important advantage. They do not need any piers or foundations, thus avoiding the biggest technical problem of bridge construction. They can be quickly assembled over any body of water, no matter how deep or how unstable the underwater bed may be.

Because of this, *pontoon bridges*, as they are called, are useful in warfare. When a bridge has been destroyed to halt an advancing army—or where no bridge exists—the military engineers can rapidly assemble a floating bridge on which an army can cross. It need have no great permanence, so long as it serves the military need of the moment.

Hundreds of pontoon bridges were built during World War

II. But the idea is by no means a recent one. Men were crossing the Tigris and Euphrates Rivers on floating bridges three thousand years ago, and still do. A celebrated pontoon bridge played an important role in a great war of 2,500 years ago, the struggle between Persia and Greece.

In that conflict, powerful Persia attempted to crush small, stubbornly determined Greece. Persia's King Xerxes invaded Greece in 481 B.C. at the head of a vast army. His legions halted at Abydos while Xerxes' Phoenician and Egyptian engineers built a bridge to carry them across the Hellespont, the strait that separates Asia and Europe.

It was a double pontoon bridge, Herodotus tells us: "While the Phoenicians constructed one line with cables of white flax, the Egyptians in the other used ropes made of papyrus. Now it is about a mile across from Abydos to the opposite coast. When, therefore, the channel had been bridged successfully, it happened that a great storm arising broke the whole work to pieces, and destroyed all that had been done."

Xerxes was furious at the delay. In his wrath, he ordered that the Hellespont should receive 300 lashes, and that a pair of fetters be cast into it. "Nay," Herodotus writes, "I have even heard it said, that he bade the branders take their irons and therewith brand the Hellespont."

Having vented his displeasure in this way, Xerxes still had the problem of getting his soldiers across the strait. His engineers tried again. Once more they constructed a pontoon bridge, using a line of boats as the floating piers to carry the cables on which the road would be mounted. But they fashioned more elaborate cables this time. Here is Herodotus' account of the process:

"They joined together triremes and fifty-oared ships, 360 to support the bridge on the side of the Euxine Sea, and 314 to sustain the other; and these they placed at right angles to the sea, and in the direction of the current of the Hellespont, relieving by these means the tension of the shore cables.

"Having joined the vessels, they moored them with anchors of unusual size. . . . A gap was left in the fifty-oared ships and triremes, to afford a passage for such light craft as chose to enter or leave the Euxine. When all this was done, they made the cables taut from the shore by the help of wooden capstans.

"This time, moreover, instead of using the two materials separately, they assigned to each bridge six cables, two of which were of white flax, while four were of papyrus. Both cables were of the same size and quality; but the flaxen were the heavier, weighing not less than fifty pounds per foot. When the bridge across the channel was thus complete, trunks of trees were sawn into planks, which were cut to the width of the bridge, and these were laid side by side upon the tightened cables, and then fastened at the top. This done, brushwood was brought, and arranged upon the planks, after which earth was heaped upon the brushwood, and the whole trodden down into a solid mass. Lastly a bulwark was set up on either side of this causeway, of such a height as to prevent the beasts of burden and the horses from seeing over it and taking fright at the water."

The troops of Xerxes proceeded to cross this bridge laid on a foundation of ships. It took seven days and seven nights for the great army to cross, marching without rest or pause. Xerxes' engineers deserve high marks for their ingenuity and craftsmanship. But the Greeks won the war, all the same.

2:

The Romans Show the World How

THE PERSIAN EMPIRE WENT THE WAY OF SUMERIA AND ASSYRIA AND Babylonia. The Greeks, split by civil strife, slipped from greatness. Egypt entered into decline after three thousand years of magnificence.

The old captains and kings departed, and a new breed of masters came to the world. Moving outward from their Italian homeland, the Romans made themselves the overlords of the known universe. From Spain to India, from the frozen north to the torrid Sahara, the Roman eagle rose in triumph. For half a thousand years, these peculiarly efficient, wonderfully well organized Romans ruled the world.

The Romans wrote no plays to equal those of the Greek Sophocles. Their philosophers did not approach lofty Plato and wise Socrates. Roman sculpture is only a poor imitation of the Greek masterpieces. Roman painting is crude compared with the brilliant work of Egypt. Roman science seems timid and faltering by the side of the knowledge the Babylonians had.

But the Romans were engineers. They could build. They built well, and they built for the ages. Twenty centuries after the great days of Rome, Europe and Africa still display monuments of Roman engineering skill: temples, aqueducts, roads, towers, and bridges. Bridges were essential to the Roman idea of power. The strength of the Roman Empire lay in its tight-knit communication channels, in the masterful network of roads that bound the far-flung provinces together. Where there are roads, there must be bridges to span the ravines and rivers.

The Romans learned about bridges, it seems, from the Etruscans, that mysterious people who inhabited Italy before Rome's rise to glory. The Etruscans, who may have migrated to Italy from Asia Minor, knew the secret of the arch, an invention of the Sumerians. They employed the arch as the pattern for their own bridges. The Romans, always quick to devour the knowledge of an older race, adapted the arch idea from the Etruscans and expanded on it.

The oldest Roman bridge, according to tradition, was the Pons Sublicius, named for the *sublicae,* or wooden beams, from which it was fashioned. Ancus Marcius, a semilegendary king of Rome, is said to have built the Pons Sublicius across the Tiber River in 621 B.C. It was this bridge—the only one leading to Rome in those early days—which the hero Horatius defended against Etruscan invaders, in the tale immortalized by Macaulay's poem:

> *In yon strait path a thousand*
> *May well be stopped by three.*
> *Now who will stand on either hand,*
> *And keep the bridge with me?*

Bridge-building had powerful religious significance to the Romans of Horatius' day. To build a bridge was to offend the god of the river, since it meant a violation of his territory. To gratify the irritated god, the Romans at first practiced human sacrifice each year, casting a victim from the bridge into the river. Later, dummies made of rushes and known as *argei* were used instead to propitiate the god. Then, too, the Pons Sublicius was built of wood, since the Romans thought a relatively flimsy wooden bridge would give less offense to the river god than a permanent one of stone. When the force of the rushing river had weakened the bridge, it was reconstructed using stone piers—but the deck remained of wood, and not even a nail was used in its construction.

Human sacrifice, which the Romans early outgrew, remained a part of bridge-building in many areas of the world. Chinese bridges claimed human lives this way, and in outlying regions of China animals still are sacrificed when a bridge is built or when it is threatened by flood. In Mexico, under Aztec rule, sacrifices of humans were common in bridge work. And Sir Mark Sykes, who traveled widely in the Orient before World War I, wrote of a Turkish bridge which had collapsed three times during construction. " 'This bridge needs a life,' said the workmen. And the master saw a beautiful girl, accompanied by a dog and her puppies, and he said, 'We will give the first life that comes by.' But the dog and her little ones hung back, so the girl was built alive into the bridge, and only her hand with a gold bracelet upon it was left outside."

The Romans had a good military reason, as well as a religious one, for building the Pons Sublicius out of wood. That way, it could be deliberately destroyed with ease in case of attack, leaving the enemies stranded on the far bank. While Horatius and his two brave companions were holding off the Etruscan army, the Romans were busily chopping down the bridge behind them—so that the last of the three defenders had to swim for his life when the bridge finally fell into the Tiber.

The Romans appointed six public officials to see that the Pons Sublicius remained in a good state of repair. These officials bore the title of *Pontifex*, or "bridge-builder," and their chief was called the *Pontifex Maximus*. Eventually, the *Pontifex Maximus* became the chief religious functionary of ancient Rome, his bridge-building duties forgotten along the way. From the time of Augustus Caesar on, the Roman Emperor automatically held the honorary title of *Pontifex Maximus*. It has survived the Roman Empire itself, for today the Pope is still referred to as the Pontiff—a title that goes back 2,600 years, to the Roman officials responsible for repairing the Pons Sublicius.

Roman Engineering Techniques

The Pons Sublicius was swept away by a flood in A.D. 69, and we do not even know today where its exact location was. In the six centuries of its life, however, the Romans made vast strides in the art of bridge-building. Overlooking their religious scruples, they abandoned timber bridges in favor of substantial bridges of stone. Stone bridges, if they were to be of any real size, required that the arch be perfected and employed.

The arch, as invented by the Sumerians, had been constructed of rows of horizontally placed bricks. It was a corbelled arch— that is, each row of bricks was supported by the one below it, and reached slightly further toward the middle of the arch. This provided the essential advantage of the arch, the outward thrust, but not the solidity of a truly rounded arch. The Romans, following the lead of the Etruscans, used the stronger semicircular arch.

This was made from bricks or stone blocks that had a tapering wedge-shaped form. These building blocks, known as *voussoirs,* can be arranged at angles that gradually widen toward the central stone, or keystone. An arch built of *voussoirs* exerts not only a downward weight but an outward one. It has a tendency to spread or "thrust." In order to hold such an arch together, the Romans originally were forced to place heavy abutments or buttresses at either end. Each *voussoir* thrust against its neighbor, and the overall thrust was transmitted to the abutments and thence to the ground. This was a technique the Romans learned from the Etruscans.

By the time of Julius Caesar, though, the Romans had found a better method. They used concrete to hold their arches together. *Pozzolana,* a red volcanic earth found at Puteoli (Pozzuoli) near Naples, was mixed in a kiln with limestone—two parts of *pozzolana* to one of lime. The result was a concrete that set quickly and with almost imperishable hardness, even under water. No better concrete was invented until the 19th century.

To make arches, the Roman engineers would build a centering, either a temporary one of wood or a permanent one of brick, to hold the sections of the arch in place until the entire structure was complete. (An incomplete arch, left unsupported at one end, would necessarily collapse.) If the arch were to be made of *voussoirs,* the wedge-shaped blocks would be fitted in place on the centering, which could then be removed once the last *voussoir* was inserted.

In the later method of making concrete arches, the Romans would spread their superb liquid concrete over the brick centering to give it strength, and afterward would face it with stone or tile.

As we have noted, the early Roman bridges were entirely of timber, or of timber across stone piers. As the Romans extended their mastery of the stone arch, they replaced many of these timbered bridges. In a typical Roman bridge, a road led to an earthen embankment that formed the approach to the bridge itself. For narrow streams, a single arching span was enough to bridge the gap. Since there are limits to the length of a stone arch that will support its own weight, broader rivers required a series of spans—half a dozen or more arches, each curving from pier to pier. The arches were always semicircular and some of them rose to great heights. There were Roman bridges as high as 160 feet, with arches of 140-foot span. (By comparison, the largest stone arch bridge built in modern times, the Plauen Bridge in Germany, completed in 1903, has a span of 295 feet.) The piers of the multi-arched Roman bridges were always built thick and strong, averaging a width of about a third of the span of the arch. With such construction each span of a bridge was strong enough to stand so long as its own two piers were intact, and the destruction of one arch would not bring down the entire bridge.

The Romans were the best engineers of their era, but they were not absolutely perfect. Strangely, they often had trouble making exact measurements. This can be seen on the oldest bridge in Rome that is still standing intact, the Pons Fabricius, built in 62 B.C. by an engineer named Lucius Fabricius. This bridge has two main arches which were obviously intended to be identical. Yet one span measures 24.24 meters, and the other measures 24.50 meters—a deviation that no modern engineer would permit!

Once they had perfected their semicircular arch, the Romans stuck to it without ever experimenting with a different form. This cost them much extra work. Their bridges would not have had to be so massive if they had used an elliptical arch instead—that is, one with a much flatter slope. The elliptical arch transmits its weight to its abutments much more efficiently than the semicircular arch, and so does not need to be so thick in order to support itself. The thick piers and ponderous arches of Roman bridges are impressive sights, but they indicate a lack of imagination.

The Romans also had problems with the foundations of their bridges. The piers of a bridge across a narrow stream can be laid on dry land, but the piers of a multi-arched bridge must be laid under water, and this stymied the Romans again and again. We have seen how, in Herodotus' account, Queen Nitocris dammed up the Euphrates so her Babylonian bridge-builders could work in a dry riverbed. But damming a river is often a colossal job in itself, and for the Romans it was frequently impossible to "turn off" the broad rivers across which they wished to build bridges.

To erect underwater piers in such cases, the Romans made use of *cofferdams*. A cofferdam is a temporary dam, usually built from timber piles. Working in shallow water, the Romans drove the piles into the riverbed around the intended site of their piers, and lined the rows of piles with clay to make them watertight. Then the interior of the cofferdam could be pumped out with a waterwheel, and concrete poured in to form the pier. When the bed of the river was soft and yielding, the Romans would sometimes build a "floor" by driving a great many piles into the muck, erecting their stone piers atop them. According to Vitruvius, the great Roman engineer, these piles were charred to keep them from rotting, and were driven into the riverbed by a machine—an early version of the pile driver.

When the water was deeper, the operation became more difficult. The Romans tried to find naturally shallow places in the river for their piers, even if this meant having to erect the piers at unequal distances from each other. That would spoil the beauty of the bridge, but beauty was a secondary consideration. Where the riverbed was too deep for workmen at all points, the solution was to drop concrete blocks to the bottom to create an artificial floor. Aristotle says that divers were used to guide the positioning of these blocks. Another method was to build frameworks of timber and lower them to the river floor, where divers could fill them with rock to form the foundation for the pier.

These methods were excellent for their day, but the Romans tended to be careless about building their foundations. Very often they did not drive the foundation deep enough into the riverbed to provide a sturdy underpinning for the spans of the bridge. They rarely took adequate precautions to keep their piers from being undermined by water action, either. The Romans were plagued constantly by piers settling into the mud or collapsing through undermining, and their bridges had to be rebuilt many times over. Yet where the underlying riverbed was strong and the engineering work was done correctly, the bridges of the Romans were all but eternal.

Some Famous Roman Bridges

Time has been kind to many of the engineering triumphs of the Romans, both in the city of Rome and elsewhere. Between 200 B.C. and A.D. 260 they built eight stone bridges across the Tiber, and six of these are still standing, having survived not only the natural ravages of time but the repeated onslaught of war. The most celebrated of these was completed in A.D. 134 by the Emperor Hadrian. This is the Aelius Bridge, which—still in use today—is now called the Ponte Sant' Angelo.

The Aelius Bridge crossed the Tiber at a point where it is particularly narrow (and therefore fast-flowing) as well as deep. Its construction must have been an enormous engineering challenge 1,800 years ago. Originally, its roadway, 34 feet wide, rested atop seven arches, the longest one spanning about 60 feet. The river was partly dammed during the laying of the foundation piers, which are of great size and strength and which are said to reach 16 feet below the riverbed.

Those original piers are still in use. The roadway of Hadrian's time, however, collapsed on December 19, 1450, when stampeding crowds coming from St. Peter's Cathedral rushed across it in a wild horde. It was rebuilt soon afterward, and was widened and redecorated in the 17th century.

Hadrian was a great bridge-builder, but an even greater one was his predecessor, the Emperor Trajan. One of Trajan's most famous bridges was the one over the Danube, designed in A.D. 104 by the Syrian engineer Apollodorus. This bridge no longer exists, but its piers lasted until they were removed about a century ago.

The Danube Bridge of Trajan had stone piers but timber arches. According to the historian Dio Cassius, there were twenty piers of hewn stone, each 150 feet high, 60 feet wide, and 50 feet thick. Each of the twenty timber arches was 110 feet long. The bridge spanned the Danube at a point where the river is almost three-quarters of a mile across.

This bridge—which is depicted on Trajan's Column in Rome— must have been one of the most spectacular works of the ancient world. It lasted only 30 years, though. The Romans destroyed it themselves, to keep the barbaric Dacians from crossing it into Roman territory. Not till the 19th century was the Danube bridged again.

Another bridge of Trajan's which has had a happier fate is the wonderful Alcántara across the Tagus River in Spain. (The name is derived from the Arabic words *al kantarah*, "the bridge.") This superb bridge, the work of the builder Caius Julius Lacer, was completed in A.D. 98. E. T. A. Wigram, a traveler who visited it almost exactly 1,800 years later, wrote of it:

"All is vast and huge and desolate; the sun itself hardly shows in such a picture; yet in the midst one object catches the eye which seems to challenge comparison even with nature itself—the work of Titans rather than men—The Bridge—Al Kantarah. Spain is the land of bridges. In all Europe they have few rivals, but here they own a King. Since the day when Caius Julius Lacer finished his great work for the Emperor Trajan, and was laid to rest beside it, no other bridge has ever challenged comparison with this—a work to vie with the Pyramids of Egypt or the Flavian Amphitheatre at Rome."

Pontem perpetui mansuram in saeculi mundi, Caius Julius Lacer declared when he built the Alcántara: "I have left a bridge that shall remain for eternity." It was not an idle boast. The bridge was fashioned of fine granite, and the *voussoirs* were cut and placed with such precision that no mortar was necessary. The six vast arches vault across the river at a height never less than 100 feet, towering at one point 150 feet above the water. The arches extend for 630 feet in all; the largest of them is 96 feet long. There is little ornamentation on the bridge; there it stands, unadorned, its beauty that of sheer simplicity.

The Romans left no record of how this colossus was built. The granite piers, 30 feet square, are bedded in solid rock. Some of the arch stones weigh eight tons apiece, and must have been lifted to their 150-foot height by an ingenious crane, but we can only guess at the exact method.

If not for the folly of man, the Alcántara would stand today as the Romans built it. In 1214, one of the lesser arches was breached by the Moors in their war against the Spaniards. Six hundred years later, the army of Napoleon, retreating through Spain in flight from the British, cruelly smashed the largest of the arches to halt the Duke of Wellington's advance. (The British slung a suspension bridge across the gap and safely transported their heavy guns to the other side.)

Since then, the great bridge has been repaired, with granite from the same quarry Caius Julius Lacer used. Its original beauty has been restored. The restorers, though, were unable to equal the craftsmanship of Trajan's engineers in one respect: they found that it was necessary to use mortar to reconstruct the shattered arches, where Lacer had needed none.

A Roman bridge known to every high school student who ever struggled with Caesar's *De Bello Gallico* is the one across the Rhine, built in 55 B.C. Writing of himself in the third person, Caesar relates that he "had determined to cross the Rhine, but a crossing by means of boats seemed to him both too risky, and beneath his dignity as a Roman commander. Therefore, although the construction of a bridge presented very great difficulties on account of the breadth, depth, and swiftness of the stream, he decided that he must either attempt it or give up the idea of crossing."

Caesar's Rhine Bridge was founded on groups of four thick wooden piles driven slantwise into the riverbed in two pairs set 40 feet apart. "The two pairs," he wrote, "were then joined by a beam two feet wide, whose ends fitted exactly into the spaces between the two piles forming each pair. The upper pair was kept

Pont du Gard near Nimes, France, the most splendid surviving Roman aqueduct.

at the right distance from the lower pair by means of iron braces, one of which was used to fasten each pile to the end of the beam. The pairs of the piles being thus held apart, and each pair individually strengthened by a diagonal tie between the two piles, the whole structure was so rigid that, in accordance with the laws of physics, the greater the force of the current, the more tightly were the piles held in position." A series of these piles and crossbeams was carried right across the river, and then logs were laid along them to form the roadbed of the bridge. Other piles were fixed on the downstream side of the bridge to break the force of the current, and on the upstream side to fend off the shock of tree trunks launched by the enemy to destroy the bridge.

"Ten days after the collection of the timber had begun," Caesar tells us proudly, "the work was completed and the army crossed over."

The Roman bridges we have been discussing were intended mainly for the movements of armies. Fresh running water was nearly as important to the Romans as military conquest, though, and some of the greatest Roman bridges were aqueducts, designed to carry not people but a water supply. Aqueducts usually were overland bridges, built so they ran on a slight slope that would enable the force of gravity to bring water toward a city from a mountain spring. In the time of the Caesars, the city of Rome had eleven great aqueducts that supplied the capital with more than 250 million gallons of water a day.

The most splendid surviving Roman aqueduct is the Pont du Gard, near Nimes in France. Marcus Vipsanius Agrippa, the son-in-law of Emperor Augustus, is credited with building this spectacular structure. The Pont du Gard, stretching across the valley of the River Gard for 860 feet, is a three-tiered bridge that reaches a height of 155 feet above the river. The lowest tier consists of six large arches, 51 to 80 feet in span. They serve as the support for a second tier of eleven equally large arches. This second tier has more arches than the first because, standing higher in the V-shaped valley, it must cover a greater distance from side to side. Atop it is the third tier, made up of 35 arches of 15-foot spans. This topmost tier carries the water channel, about 4 feet wide and 6 feet high, a stone pipe carefully cemented and covered on top by neat slabs. Only on this tier was cement used at all; the great arches below it were formed from stones cut exactly to shape, each resting against its neighbor in a perfect fit that needs no binding mortar. The Pont du Gard was seriously damaged in the 18th century, through a foolish attempt to convert it from an aqueduct to a roadway, and if the work had not been halted in time the bridge undoubtedly would have collapsed. In 1855 it was restored to its original state of grandeur.

The aqueduct at Nimes marked an engineering advance for the Romans, who constructed it with unusually thin, graceful piers. The piers of the Pont du Gard are only a fifth as thick as the arch spans are long, instead of the customary one to three ratio of pier thickness to span length. This accomplishment was surpassed a few generations later, in the reign of Trajan, when the aqueduct of Segovia was built in Spain. This aqueduct, 2,700 feet long and 119 feet high, has two tiers of arches of equal span, but the lower tier is supported by slender piers just eight feet thick— a one to eight ratio.

The Romans, at their best, built bridges of monumental strength and striking beauty. Their engineering triumphs long outlasted their own empire.

3:

Bridges of The Middle Ages

THE GREAT AGE OF ROMAN ENGINEERING WAS OVER BY A.D. 300. Pressed on all sides by unruly barbarians, the Romans drew back, unable to sustain the weight of their own power any longer. Bridges and roads and aqueducts fell into disrepair. In A.D. 410 Alaric, of the tribe called the Goths, led a barbarian army into the capital city of Rome itself, and set it aflame. Roman authority was shattered. The vast European empire broke apart.

Now began the period we call the Dark Ages. They were not as dark as some people think, for, although the bright light of Rome was extinguished, there was a slow but steady spread of learning in western Europe. The fierce warriors who had overthrown Rome were becoming civilized themselves, and out of the turmoil of the Dark Ages would come the new leaders of Europe in France and England and Germany.

But the years from A.D. 400 to 1200 were years of political upheaval, of wars and chaos, and in such conditions it is rare that bridges are built. Only a well-organized people, directed by a strong central authority, can undertake the giant effort of building a bridge. In a Europe torn by the conflicts of petty princelings, the engineering arts were neglected and the mighty bridges of the Romans stood as reproaches to the men of later centuries.

By the year 1200, though, powerful new nations had taken form in Europe, and bridges were built once more. Kings and barons demanded bridges to foster trade within their territories and to permit the free movements of travelers. England in particular became a bridge-building nation; for, when William the Conqueror and his Normans took possession of England in 1066, they divided the land in such a way that no one nobleman had a large compact domain. William shrewdly gave his barons many small holdings scattered all over the country. So that they could travel easily to inspect their estates, the Norman barons desired that bridges be built and kept in good repair. This was just the opposite of the situation in France, where each high nobleman ruled over a huge estate that was practically a kingdom in itself. These feudal lords were often at war with one another, and found it to their advantage to oppose the building of bridges that could give an enemy army access to their territory. Thus many more bridges were built in medieval England than in medieval France. Each nation, though, had its share of great bridges.

London Bridge

Despite the famous jingle, London Bridge never did fall down. It stood for six hundred years, tottering most of the time but always holding together. A more fantastic, unlikely, ungainly bridge would be hard to imagine. London Bridge was an engineer's nightmare, an impossible bridge, crazy and awkward. But Londoners loved it, and tore it down only when common sense finally triumphed over sentiment.

The Thames River, flowing eastward to the sea, provided a natural site for a settlement. When the Romans under Emperor Claudius invaded Britain in A.D. 43, they picked the site of London as an ideal base for the conquest of the island, and built a camp they called *Londinium.* Coming northward toward the Thames, the Romans must have been stopped only momentarily by the river. If Julius Caesar had bridged the Rhine in 10 days a century earlier, it could not have been too difficult for Claudius' engineers to bridge the Thames. Londinium grew into a wealthy city, with houses on both sides of the river.

When the Romans withdrew from Britain after A.D. 400, Londinium vanished from history's annals. Archaeologists are not sure what sort of life the city had in the following centuries, but by the year 1000 it was again thriving and soon was the most important city in the land. Wooden bridges were erected across the Thames, but, like most wooden bridges, these were short-lived. London's growing importance demanded the construction of a permanent stone bridge. At last, in 1176, work began on the building of London Bridge.

The engineer in charge was Peter of Colechurch, a priest who had helped to build the last timber bridge on the Thames a few years earlier. No one knew better than Peter how difficult his new assignment would be. The river was 900 feet wide at London, and its bed was muddy. To provide an extra complication, ocean tides came roaring westward into the mouth of the Thames every twelve hours, the salty water flowing back to the sea just as swiftly as it came, twice a day. The daily range of water level from low tide to high tide was 16 feet.

It took a patient man to build a stone bridge under such conditions. Peter's approach was to take advantage of the seasons, working in dry weather when the river was low, adding one arch at a time until the bridge was finished. The job took thirty-three years, and Peter of Colechurch did not live to see its completion.

London Bridge did not differ in any essential way from a typical Roman bridge. Stone piers supported arches of unequal spans. Instead of the Roman semicircular arch, Peter used the pointed arch, which was easier to construct because it placed less load on the wooden centering while being built. Timber cofferdams were driven into the riverbed and filled with stones to serve as the foundations of the piers. Gordon Home, who wrote a classic history of London Bridge in 1931, vividly described the way the pile drivers hammered the cofferdam timbers into place:

"Loungers . . . would have watched the long winding up followed by the sudden drop of the heavy weights which inch by inch brought the pile down to the level of low water. They would have watched the hoisting of the blocks of stone from the barges, the difficulty of getting the lowest course of masonry placed on the foundations just exposed at low tide, and the pouring in of hot pitch, and later on would have seen the carpenters fixing their wooden centering upon which were placed the carefully shaped *voussoirs* of the arch stones.''

It took 18 months, on the average, to complete each arch. As the row of piers grew, the water of the river rushed much more rapidly through the narrowing space left to it, and the work became more hazardous. Hundreds of workmen lost their lives during the construction. There were 19 arches in all. The original plan called for all the arches to have a 28-foot span, except for one double-length arch in the center of the bridge, and for all the piers to be 20 feet wide. As it turned out, the spacing of the piers was exceedingly lopsided, to take advantage of the varying riverbed conditions. No two piers or arches were alike in the finished bridge. The spans of the arches ranged from 15 to 34 feet, and the piers were 18 to 26 feet in width. The grand pier, whose arch spanned 95 feet, carried a two-story chapel, and served as well as an extra-heavy support for the entire bridge.

Peter of Colechurch was buried in his own chapel a few years before the completion of the bridge in 1209. The Thames had been spanned—but the result was a monstrosity. The piers were not only of all different sizes, but they were so thick that they turned the bridge virtually into a dam. The piers occupied 420 feet of the 936-foot-wide waterway, leaving only 516 feet for the water. The river had to flow through 19 small and unequal openings, which grew smaller yet with the years as repairs to the piers made them thicker. The tides, racing in out of the channel twice a day, now sped through the bridge openings at such a pace that the river became a raging torrent. And at high tide, there was only five feet of headroom between the surface of the water and the roadway of the bridge.

The effect was to strangle the shipping industry of London. Only small boats could possibly get through the openings between the piers, and steering at high tide was something like running the rapids on a wild canyon stream. The boatman, "shooting the bridge," was swept along by the furious water. He had to point his prow desperately toward an opening and hope that the turbulence did not smash him into a pier. Large cargoes had to be unloaded upriver and carried by land around the bridge to ocean-going vessels waiting downriver from the structure.

Nonetheless, Londoners hailed their new bridge fondly. To pay the cost of maintenance, the bridge authorities decided to build houses and shops along the roadway, and these quickly became desirable locations. They fronted on the roadway, reducing its already narrow width to a mere dozen feet, and overhung the river in back, supported by timber struts that went down to the piers. Some of the buildings spanned the roadway entirely, so that carts and pedestrians had to pass through a tunnel, which was really the first floor of a two-story building.

In July, 1212, three years after the opening of the bridge, fire swept through this maze of wooden houses, and thousands of lives were lost. The buildings of London Bridge were promptly restored, and in the centuries that followed they grew ever larger and more varied in their architecture. Taverns and fine jewelry shops flourished there, and many wealthy Londoners made their homes on the bridge. Now and then a building came free of its supports and toppled into the water; it was soon replaced. Frequent fires did not dismay the residents either. The burden of buildings grew and grew and grew like some strange infestation of fungus, spreading to every part of the bridge.

In 1580 a new encumberance appeared: a set of waterwheels to pump water from the river to the houses on the bridge. Four arches were blocked by these wheels, which carried 216 gallons a minute by lead pipes to the householders. The Dutch inventor who designed and installed the wheels made a fortune from his fees, but the narrow waterway was now that much more difficult to use.

A fire in 1632 burned out several houses in the middle of the bridge. They were not immediately rebuilt, which proved a lucky thing; for in 1666 nearly all of London on the north side of the bridge was devastated by fire. The fire destroyed the bridge's clutter of houses as far as the burned-out gap, but could not spread across the gap to the south side of the river. After the Great Fire of 1666, the roadway was repaired and widened, and new houses in more modern style were built. London Bridge was getting creaky, though.

It became a slum as the fashionable tenants moved out and the mansions were divided into small apartments. In the 1740's, a second stone bridge was finally built across the Thames to the west, and by 1757 London Bridge was given a major face-lifting to make it more useful. The houses were removed and the roadway widened again. In hopes of eliminating the navigational bottleneck created by the weird old bridge, engineers removed the central pier and converted two small arches into one big one.

It was a mistake. The work weakened the adjoining piers, and the violent rush of the water threatened to pull the whole bridge down. "London Bridge is broken down," Londoners sang, in an early version of the nursery rhyme. Arches were rebuilt, piers were strengthened, the old bridge of Peter of Colechurch unrecognizable now—and still the tottering bridge remained an obstacle to navigation and a menace to all who crossed it. Reluctantly, London admitted that it was time to remove the ridiculous, beloved antiquity. In 1831, when a new London Bridge was completed, the remains of Peter of Colechurch's miraculous monster were cleared from the river.

The Pont d'Avignon

In 1177, one year after work on London Bridge began, a master builder of France undertook the construction of a bridge across the Rhône at Avignon. As lovely as the bridge of Peter of Colechurch was clumsy, the Pont d'Avignon won a place for itself in nursery rhymes and gained the admiration of all engineers.

A legend tells of a total eclipse of the sun that darkened the sky over the prosperous town of Avignon on a September day. The townspeople, frightened, gathered in the marketplace. The bishop appeared and began to preach a sermon, when suddenly a ragged youth ran forward. Boldly interrupting the bishop's words, the boy cried out that the eclipse was a sign from God, who had commanded him to build a great bridge. The sun returned; and the boy, whose name was Bénoît, lifted an immense stone and carried it to the river's edge as the first block of his bridge. The people of Avignon, recognizing that only the hand of God could have enabled the boy to carry such a boulder, commissioned Bénoît to build the bridge.

It is a pretty story, and, whether true or not, the bridge that Bénoît built was a masterpiece. The Rhône was a challenging river to span, for it was wide and deep, and its level could rise more than 25 feet at the time of the rushing spring floods. Bénoît chose a site where the river is split into two channels by an island. He erected a series of lofty arches, each with a span greater than 100 feet, rising on piers 25 feet thick. There were about 20 arches in all—the exact number is unknown today—and the bridge was nearly 3,000 feet long. That made it the longest bridge since Roman times, and, except for a few aqueducts, the longest stone bridge ever built.

It had grace and dignity as well as size. The slender arches were rounded, not pointed as in London Bridge. Their curve, though, was not the old Roman semicircle, but a flatter, more elliptical one that allowed the piers to be set farther apart. That had the advantage of keeping the water open to shipping, and also minimized the damming effect that was so disastrous on the Thames. In a further attempt to reduce the effects of the strong current, Bénoît put an elbow-bend in the western branch of his bridge, causing it to turn at a 30 degree angle upstream against the flow. The wide V thus formed was better able to take the thrust of the current than a straight bridge.

The lofty Pont d'Avignon, with its towering arches and wide-set piers, carried a strangely narrow roadway, only 16 feet wide at its broadest point. Near the Avignon side of the bridge, the road was only six and a half feet wide, the rest of the space being taken up by a chapel. Carts and coaches could not pass across the bridge, but only pedestrians and horsemen. Bénoît, master engineer that he was, could have built a wider roadway had he wished. But it was a suspicious age, and Avignon demanded a road that could easily be defended against invaders. A handful of men stationed at the narrowest part of the bridge could hold it against a vast army.

Bénoît died in 1184 and was buried, like Peter of Colechurch, in the chapel of his own bridge. Three years later the great bridge was completed. The fierce floods of the Rhône did not harm the

Pont d'Avignon, spanning the Rhône River at Avignon, France. Begun in 1177, and completed ten years later; now after eight centuries, the chapel, four arches and three of the boat-shaped piers still remain.

Pont d'Avignon at all, but in the 14th century one of the arches was deliberately cut to prevent an invasion of the city. It was repaired some years later, by engineers who lacked Bénoît's skill. The weakened bridge gradually became more vulnerable to the force of the river. In 1602, a strong flood knocked down the arch that had been repaired, and three adjoining arches were pulled down by its collapse. Two more arches fell in the floods of 1633, and in 1670 massive ice floes swept down the river and all but completed the job of destruction. Only four arches, on the eastern branch of the bridge, survived. Restoring the bridge was too great a task for Avignon to undertake, but the four magnificent arches of the ruin were allowed to remain, as a memorial to the lost greatness of the medieval bridge.

The Late Middle Ages

London Bridge and the Pont d'Avignon were the early har-
bingers of a wondrous era of bridge-building. The cities of western
Europe were thriving, now, and the growth of commerce demanded
new bridges. So far as methods of construction went, the bridges
of the 14th and 15th centuries followed the practices of the Romans. The arch bridge of stone was still the only possible design
for a large bridge, and the technique of using cofferdams to construct the pier foundations had not changed since the time of the
Caesars. The only innovation was the elliptical arch, which permitted less massive, more graceful bridges to be erected.

In Italy, the bustling city of Florence had emerged as a commercial center under the inspired leadership of its ambitious family
of dukes, the Medici. The goldsmiths of Florence fashioned jewelry
sought in every land, while sumptuous garments of wool came
from the Florentine factories. In 1345, Florence's growing trade
connections made necessary the building of a stone bridge across
the River Arno.

The Arno was 300 feet wide at the site where the builder,
Taddeo Gaddi, chose to put the bridge. He experimented with the
new elliptical arch and needed only two piers to carry his bridge,
with a central span of 100 feet and a pair of 90-foot side spans.
Above the roadway rose a two-story arcade. The lower story contained the shops of jewelers and goldsmiths; the upper was a covered
passageway linking the two opulent palaces, the Pitti and Uffizi,
on opposite sides of the river. Taddeo Gaddi's bridge was joined
in time by three other medieval bridges on the Arno, so that it
became known as the Ponte Vecchio, "the old bridge." It was completed in 1367. Its handsome neighbor, the Ponte Santa Trinità,
finished almost exactly two hundred years later, followed the Ponte
Vecchio's example of employing unusually low, sweeping arches.
The Santa Trinità, with three arches of white marble, was so
slender in its long spans and slim piers that the drivers of heavy
vehicles hesitated at first to use it. Yet it survived without incident
until World War II, when German soldiers blew it up in a criminal
act of military vandalism. The Ponte Vecchio, still bearing its

Ponte Vecchio in Florence, Italy, completed in 1367, still spans the Arno River.

medieval shops, was happily spared by the Nazi demolition teams. After the war, the bereaved Florentines dredged the stones of the Santa Trinità from the Arno and painstakingly rebuilt the bridge in an exact replica of its original form.

The increasing skill of bridge-builders allowed them to work wonders with the basic stone arch form in the late medieval period. A daring Italian bridge across the River Adda had a single stone span of 236 feet. This bridge, completed in 1371, had by far the longest stone arch ever constructed up till then, surpassing the best Roman effort by more than 100 feet. But a single-span stone bridge could be destroyed too easily, and the form never became popular.

Paris got its first bridge in 1507: the Pont Notre Dame. It was built in record time, seven years, after the collapse in 1499 of the timber bridge that connected the Île de la Cité in the Seine with the mainland. This small island was the original heart of the city, founded by Gallic tribesmen in Roman times; when the Romans conquered it in 52 B.C., they spread their settlements to the left bank of the Seine, and about A.D. 300 the right bank was occupied as well. Timber bridges linked the Île de la Cité with both banks, and the island remained the central core of Paris. When Christianity reached France, a cathedral was founded on the island— the ancestor of the mighty Cathedral of Notre Dame, which dominates the island today.

An Italian engineer, Fra Giovanni Giocondo, was imported to build a permanent stone bridge linking the cathedral island with the rest of the city. Though he quarreled with his French assistants over the planning of the bridge, Giocondo speedily reared a six-arch structure, the four inner arches having spans of 57 feet. Cofferdams were pumped dry by wheels turned by plodding horses, and heavy tree trunks were driven into the riverbed, with stone piers erected on dry foundations of concrete within the cofferdams. When the Pont Notre Dame was torn down in 1853 to be replaced by a modern bridge, the piers were found to be so sturdy after 350

Ponte Santa Trinità in Florence, Italy, built in the sixteenth century, it survived almost without incident until it was destroyed during World War II. After the war, the bereaved Florentines rebuilt the bridge in an exact replica of its original form.

Le Pont Neuf, meaning "the new bridge," constructed during the sixteenth century, is today by pleasant irony the oldest surviving bridge in Paris.

years that they were used for the new bridge, and two of them still remain in the newer Pont Notre Dame of 1913.

Seventy years after the completion of Giocondo's Notre Dame Bridge, a new link was forged, this time between the downstream end of the Île de la Cité and both banks of the Seine. This was the Pont Neuf, or "the new bridge," which by a pleasant irony is now the oldest surviving bridge in Paris. The Pont Neuf reaches in two directions, a long arm of seven arches going to the right bank and a short arm of five arches to the left. Work started in 1578, and the foundations for the piers of the short arm were in place within a year. It was the haste that makes waste, however, and the speedy work had to be done over.

A massive bridge must be founded on a solid base. The floor of the Seine was soft mud. Only 10 feet below the mud was the underlying rock, which would have provided an ideal support for the piers. Mysteriously, the engineers decided not to dig down to rock, but to found their piers on a timber grillwork resting atop the mud.

The first step, as usual, was to drive timber piles into the river-bed to form a cofferdam. If these piles had been driven down to the bedrock, all would have been well. But they were driven only a few feet into the mud. At that point, the builders decided that the point of "refusal" had been reached—that is, the point at which the piles could be driven no deeper. Even with the crude and in-efficient pile-driving machines of the 16th century, it seems as though the engineers gave up too quickly. When the cofferdams were finished and made watertight, they were pumped dry and timber beams were laid across the subsoil. The heavy stonework of the piers rested on this wooden grillwork.

There were two dangers in this. The foundations, once they bore the weight of the completed bridge, might settle a foot or more as they packed down the mud beneath them, unbalancing the bridge. Also the piers were vulnerable to "scour," the cutting action of water-swept sand. Moving sand in a swift river could slice away at the underlying pilings and bring the whole pier down. Only if the piles reached to bedrock could scour be avoided.

Work on the Pont Neuf was interrupted by war after just the

pier foundations had been laid. By the time Paris was ready to re-
sume construction, two of the piers had been so badly undermined
by scour that they were useless. New cofferdams had to be built
on the upstream sides of the piers, and within them more piles were
driven, anchored to the original piers by iron clamps to protect
them against scour. Even so, the new piles still were not driven to
the real point of refusal at bedrock.

The arches now were constructed, and in 1607 the bridge
was opened. Rows of little shops were built along the roadway,
and it became one of the busiest centers of Parisian life. The piers
slowly settled into the mud, and the scour damage was great. Not
until 1848, though, was any serious rebuilding done. The shops
were torn down, the seven arches of the long arm were replaced
with flatter, more elliptical ones, and the long-teetering foundations were bolstered but not replaced. The five arches of the left
bank arm were allowed to keep their 17th-century form.

The problem of founding a heavy stone bridge on soft subsoil was much more acute in Venice, where the entire city rests on
a plain of mud. Venice is a city of innumerable tiny islands, and
the underlying soil is so swampy that its buildings settle a fraction
of an inch every year. Timber bridges of no great weight were
built to span the many canals, but such bridges were frequently
swept away by fire. The most important of these wooden bridges
crossed the Grand Canal in the district called the Rialto, from
rivo alto, "high bank." It was built in 1252, and had to be repaired
constantly. When a fire raced through the Rialto district in 1512
and threatened to destroy the bridge, the Venetians resolved to
replace it with one of stone.

Bridge-builders studied the site, scratched their heads, and
walked away in despair. The subsoil was spongy and could never
carry the thrust of an arch, they said. Any bridge would have to
have an extraordinary design, for it had to be high above the water
to permit free movement of boats on the Grand Canal, and yet
the waterway was so narrow that there was no room for the abutments a high arch would require. Several plans were actually
drawn, including one by Michelangelo, but nothing came of them.

The Rialto Bridge in Venice, Italy, completed in 1592, still stands today as an outstanding engineering accomplishment and as one of the world's most beautiful bridges.

Several times, a bridge design was accepted and then quietly shelved after consideration of the practical difficulties.

In 1587, an architect named Antonio da Ponte submitted a new plan for a bridge at the Rialto. Da Ponte had been born about the time the Venetians first decided to build the bridge, and he had grown old during the years of delay. Now he was past seventy, and had had a long lifetime to ponder the challenges of the site.

Da Ponte's idea was to drive thousands of wooden piles into the treacherous subsoil. Six thousand piles of birch, six inches in diameter and 11 feet long, were hammered into the mud on either side of the canal. They were driven in such tight clusters that they practically touched each other, forming a nearly solid wooden base of great size and strength. One modern engineer has pointed out that "this would not now be considered the best way to use piles, since the whole assembly could move as a solid block: fewer, longer piles more widely spaced would have spread the load better. Yet the foundations have not moved."

The piles were cut level and topped by three layers of timber fastened by iron clamps. Layers of stone were placed above these timbers and the arch itself, a single span 88 feet long, was founded on the stone abutments. Above the arch the unique roadway was placed, gently sloping upward toward the center of the bridge, with an elegant balustrade at either rim, and an arcade of shops arranged in several rows. The result was not only an outstanding engineering accomplishment but an artistic triumph, for the Rialto is one of the world's most beautiful bridges.

It was also one of the world's most expensive bridges. It cost Venice 250,000 golden ducats, an immense sum. Work was halted several times when the thrifty Venetians objected to the cost, but da Ponte persuaded them each time to let him continue. Another difficulty was provided by a jealous architect named Scamozzi, whose own plan for a bridge on a novel floating foundation was rejected. Scamozzi insisted that da Ponte's pilings would not resist the thrust of the finished arch, and his charges resulted in delays while the city fathers investigated da Ponte's work. By 1592, though, the bridge was completed and opened for traffic.

A few years later, an earthquake shook the city. The shop-keepers of the Rialto fled in panic as the bridge began to quiver. If ever Scamozzi's accusations were to be borne out, this was the moment. But when the earth had ceased to tremble, the people of Venice came forth to look at their bridge. There stood Antonio da Ponte's miracle in stone, intact and unharmed. And there it stands today.

4:

The Iron Age

BY THE MIDDLE OF THE 18TH CENTURY, BRIDGE-BUILDERS HAD CAR-
ried the arch of stone about as far as it could go. Centuries of
cautious experiment had transformed the Roman-style bridge, lofty
and massive with its thick piers and semicircular arches, into a
graceful, slender structure. The elliptical arch carried the thrust of
the bridge even when the piers were placed so far apart that a
Roman engineer would have gasped in amazement. The secret was
the overall play of forces in the bridge. The Romans were too concerned with making sure that each arch would stand erect no
matter what happened to its neighbor. The bridge-builders of the
17th and 18th centuries learned that some risks could safely be
taken—that in a wide pier bridge, each arch still had independent
strength but the thrust of all the arches was carried the length of
the bridge to the abutments at the banks. Roman caution, therefore, was not necessary.

The architect Jean Perronet, born near Paris in 1708, took
the stone arch bridge to its theoretical limits. Perronet's most startling achievement was the Neuilly Bridge across the Seine north of
Paris. He daringly reduced the thickness of the piers to less than
one-ninth the span of the arches. The piers were only 13 feet
thick, and the five equal arches of the bridge had 120-foot spans.

The result was an airy, weightless-looking bridge that seemed to soar across the river in easy leaps, pausing lightly and only momentarily at the piers. Those who viewed the bridge under construction freely made grim predictions about its fate, and harsh comments about Perronet's sanity. But when the bridge was finished in 1772 it was perfectly stable, and it carried its burdens without effort until 1956, when it was taken down to make way for a larger bridge.

Perronet died in 1794, eighty-six years old and still building bridges to the last moments of his life. The French Revolution had swept through France in his final years. But another revolution was in the making, too, which would reshape the life of Europe—the Industrial Revolution. A new era was being born, an era of belching smokestacks and sprawling factories, an era of coal and iron, an era of heavy machinery and railroad transportation. The new era no longer cared for the sort of poetry in stone that Jean Perronet had created. The times called for bridges of a new style, of a new material.

The first bugle call of the new era was sounded while Jean Perronet was still alive. In 1779 the Severn River in England was spanned by a bridge of iron.

Mankind had known the use of iron since about 1400 B.C. At first, raw iron was heated until it could be hammered into the shape of a sword or a sickle. Later, blacksmiths learned how to build fires so hot they could melt iron and cast it in molds. Cast iron was an extremely hard but brittle metal. Wrought iron, a later form that contained less carbon, had a greater tensile strength and could be heated red-hot and rolled or hammered into shape. In medieval times, wrought iron was sometimes used to strengthen the joints of large wooden structures, but it was too expensive to employ on a wide scale.

Iron Bridges

Cast iron, though it was less easily worked than wrought iron, was cheaper to produce. The world's first iron bridge, then, was made of cast iron. Thomas Farnolls Pritchard, an architect of the town of Shrewsbury, drew up a plan for such a bridge crossing the Severn at the village of Coalbrookdale. Pritchard got the backing of an ironmaster named John Wilkinson, who raised some of the money for the project. Pritchard and Wilkinson dropped out of the enterprise before it got under way, however, and responsibility for the bridge was assumed by another local ironmaster, Abraham Darby III.

Darby was less than thirty years old when he took upon himself the technical problem—and much of the expense—of building the iron bridge of Coalbrookdale. It was an arch bridge made of five semicircular cast-iron ribs rising 45 feet from the banks of the river to carry the roadbed. Only one of the main ribs was a complete arch from bank to bank; the others were support ribs that were connected to the deck of the roadway at the side of the main arch. Thus these ribs did not carry the thrust of the arch itself, but they helped to make the road more rigid. The entire bridge, including the deck, contained 378 tons of iron, a huge amount for the year 1779. The span of the bridge was 100 feet.

The pioneering Coalbrookdale Bridge still stands. In recent years its abutments have had to be strengthened, but the ironwork itself remains as it was in Abraham Darby's day. However, the Coalbrookdale Bridge never had to carry any load more taxing than a light horse-drawn vehicle. No railroad train ever thundered across it, and today automobile traffic is forbidden on the bridge. Its brittle cast-iron ribs might not be able to withstand the jarring and rattling of a high-speed vehicle.

Iron arch bridges were slow to take hold. They were cheaper to build than stone arch bridges, but engineers had many doubts about the safety of the new structural material. In the generation that followed the Coalbrookdale experiment, a few iron bridges were constructed, but most major bridges continued to be fashioned from stone.

A Scottish engineer named Thomas Telford was the man who brought about the general adoption of iron bridges. In 1784, when he was twenty-seven years old, Telford was named surveyor to the English county of Shropshire, a job that required him to maintain the county's bridges, and design new ones when necessary. His first bridge was a three-arch stone span, which still is in use.

Shropshire was a center of England's new iron industry, and in fact was the county of the Coalbrookdale Bridge. Telford studied that bridge in great fascination. When an old stone bridge across the Severn collapsed in 1795, Telford decided to replace it with an iron bridge. He improved considerably on Abraham Darby's pioneering effort, noticing that the engineers at Coalbrookdale had tried too hard to imitate the form of a stone bridge. Iron was a different material, calling for a form of its own. Telford's Buildwas Bridge on the Severn had a much flatter arch and lighter foundations than the Coalbrookdale Bridge. Though its span was greater —130 feet to the Coalbrookdale's 100—it weighed less than half as much, 173 tons.

Telford went on to build other cast-iron arch bridges, and in his growing skill he learned how to make them ever bigger and stronger. This was the time when the replacement of old London Bridge was under discussion, and Telford proposed to place one of his cast-iron arch bridges across the Thames, using 6,500 tons of iron and leaping 600 feet in a single phenomenal span. Whether such a bridge could actually have been built from brittle cast iron is a matter of some doubt. Luckily for Telford, his proposal was rejected in 1798. By 1814, an iron bridge was under construction in London, though on a less ambitious scale, with a central span of only 240 feet. It was the work of John Rennie, another convert to the use of iron. Rennie later built the replacement for London Bridge as well.

Suspension Bridges

Telford, after building many iron arch bridges, turned in 1820 to an even more radical design, one which got away from the arch principle entirely. This was the unusual 580-foot suspension bridge over the Menai Strait between the coast of Wales and the island of Anglesey.

The suspension bridge idea was nothing new; prehistoric man's bridge of vines had been a suspension bridge. Small suspension bridges hanging from iron chains had been constructed in Europe as early as the 16th century. They were flexible, flimsy affairs that whipped about madly in a high wind, and nobody had ever considered building a large suspension bridge before the 19th century.

At the beginning of that century, some American engineers experimented with such bridges. Judge James Finley of Pennsylvania received a patent in 1808 for a suspension bridge with a stiffened deck. One of his bridges, with a span of 244 feet, lasted a century; the original towers are still in use, though the roadway was rebuilt in 1909. Other Finley bridges collapsed under the weight of traffic or under loads of ice in winter, though, for the theory of building a stable suspension bridge was poorly understood.

In Scotland several suspension bridges were erected about the same time. Though they were risky, they were built because they needed only two towers, which could be founded on the shore with a long span hung between them. The arch bridge, with its severe limits on the length of span, needed many piers, and those that stood in the water were subject to undermining by winter floods. One of these Scottish bridges, completed in 1820 over the Tweed River, had a 300-foot span.

Telford, when he planned his Menai Bridge, based it on the novel design of this Tweed Bridge. He had intended to suspend his bridge from a cable made of bundles of small iron bars welded together at the ends. But the Tweed Bridge's designer, Captain Samuel Brown, invented a new kind of flat iron link chain, and Telford used this kind of cable instead. He constructed two mighty piers, standing 153 feet above the high water mark of the strait, and connected them by 16 chain cables each consisting of 935 wrought-iron bars. From these cables the roadway was suspended, a deck carrying two 12-foot-wide carriageways with a 4-foot-wide pedestrian passage between. The deck rose 100 feet above the high water level.

The breathtaking span of 580 feet far exceeded that of any other bridge. Yet it required only 2,000 tons of iron, a third as much as the recent iron arch bridge across the Thames. Would the bridge stand, though? As winds of gale force swept through the strait, the chains rattled and shook, and the roadway danced about in a frightening way. Telford braced the cables by installing crosswise fastenings. In 1839, a violent storm wrecked the wooden deck, but the cables and piers of the bridge held firm. A new and stronger timber deck was built, and lasted until 1893. Then it was replaced by a steel one. The old wrought-iron cables, still as strong as ever, remained in service until 1939, when cables of steel took their place.

The Menai Bridge was an amazing experiment, and also something of a lucky freak. Telford's brilliance created a bridge that was 60 years ahead of its time, and through his good fortune the bridge stood. Suspension bridges were the only answer when great gulfs had to be spanned, but iron was not a good enough material for such bridges. A number of suspension bridges built in the 1830's and 1840's collapsed in storms or under the stress of traffic. The great era of suspension bridges had to wait until the age of steel.

The cast-iron arch bridge, which had seemed so astonishing in 1798, was commonplace in Europe by 1840. The new bridges were strong and rigid, much more so than suspension bridges of the time. It was now possible to build a cast-iron arch sturdy enough to stand up under the pounding of a railroad train; and no engineer in his right mind would suggest a railroad bridge of the suspension type.

The railroad had arrived, and with it came the need for thousands of new bridges. The weight and vibration of a moving train created a world of unfamiliar problems for engineers. In the past, it had been good enough to build a bridge that would stand up under its own weight. So long as it would do that, the additional weight of men, horses, or carriages crossing the road was insignificant. What counted was the "dead load" of the bridge, the weight of the bridge itself, and the struggle of the engineers was to devise arches and abutments and piers that could carry that dead load. Now, for the first time, they had to plan for a "live load" as well—the very live load of tons of train, imposing terrific strains of weight and vibration. Railroad bridges were needed at every stream, every ravine, every river, and they had to be sturdier bridges than ever before.

The first experimental steam-driven vehicles were built in the late 18th century. By 1815, George Stephenson of England had a patent on a steam locomotive, and ten years later railroad lines were being built all over Great Britain. The rest of Europe and the United States were quick to follow. Railways, though, could not endure sharp turns and curves. The trains had to forge straight ahead wherever possible, no matter what obstacles blocked the path of the tracks, and that meant bridges by the thousands.

In the United States, where distances were vast, population was growing rapidly, and prosperity depended on swift communications, the railroad was a godsend. The Americans had developed a distinctive bridge form of their own, the *truss bridge,* and from the middle of the 19th century on they speedily adapted it to railroad use.

The early American colonists had needed many bridges, but they lacked the time and the resources to build stone bridges in the European fashion. It took seven years or more to construct a stone bridge of any size. European cities had had six centuries to build their many bridges. Americans needed bridges in a hurry, and that meant bridges of timber. The forests lay readily at hand. More permanent bridges could come later, the colonists agreed.

Truss Bridges

Timber arch bridges with fairly long spans had been built by the Romans before they came to favor stone, and such bridges could be used for wide rivers, while streams could always be spanned by a simple girder bridge of horizontal beams. From New England, though, came the truss form, which quickly established itself in the new colonies.

The truss is based on the triangle, a geometric form with the valuable property of rigidity. If you nail four boards together at right angles to form a square, you can push them about with ease, distorting the square into other shapes. Nail three boards together into a triangle and they cannot be pushed about at all; they may break under pressure, but their angles will never change the way those of the four-sided figure will.

Take the four-sided figure and nail a fifth board diagonally from corner to corner, and it no longer moves. The diagonal crosspiece makes the figure rigid by converting it into two triangles base to base. Put a row of triangles together back to back, so they form a structure with parallel lines at top and bottom, and it becomes a truss—a rigid structure that uses a minimum of material.

Trusses are ideal for supporting the weight of a roadway across an abyss. If the truss is placed beneath the roadway, the weight of the road puts the vertical bars, or kingposts, in a state of compression. The diagonals are thus subjected to stretching, or tension. Forces balance, the truss remains rigid, and the road is supported. If the truss is above the roadway, the kingposts are pulled down by the weight and placed in tension, but this pull squeezes the diagonals together—a state of compression—and again the forces balance.

Many varieties of truss were devised. Some seemed to have N-shaped patterns of bars, some had W-shaped patterns, some had M-shaped patterns, and so on. The basic structure of adjoining triangles could always be detected, though, and that was what gave the truss its strength.

European bridge-builders knew about the strength that lay in a chain of triangles, and occasionally built truss bridges, but the idea flowered most spectacularly in 18th-century America. An early Connecticut bridge was an arch-shaped truss with a 124-foot span. In 1792, Timothy Palmer of Massachusetts built a wooden bridge with a trussed arch of 160 feet, and a few years later another in New Hampshire that spanned 244 feet. In 1806, he constructed the "Permanent Bridge" over the Schuylkill River in Philadelphia with three wooden trussed arches totalling 550 feet.

These wooden bridges were too easily harmed by rain, snow, and the drying effects of summer heat. To protect them, the architects began to add sidings and roofs, enclosing the roadway and making it a kind of airborne tunnel. A number of these picturesque covered bridges still survive, and are treasured as local historical landmarks. One of the biggest, over the Schuylkill a few miles downstream from Timothy Palmer's bridge, was the 340-foot Fairmount Bridge of 1812. This long-vanished arched bridge used iron rods for the diagonals of the truss. It was destroyed by fire in 1838.

The truss bridge was quickly built, strong, and cheap. Over a short distance, a simple horizontal truss was enough to carry the weight. Greater spans could be managed by shaping the truss in the form of an arch, gaining the benefit of both methods. But wooden bridges were prey to fire and the work of the elements, and they were not strong enough to bear the weight of a railroad train.

The Fairmount Bridge, with its iron diagonals, showed the way toward adapting the wooden truss for railroad bridges. The next step was iron vertical members. Cast iron was too brittle to take tension well, though its strength made it suitable for the compression members. In 1847, a New Yorker named Squire Whipple invented the bowstring truss, an arched truss with the roadway beneath the curve.

The curved upper arch of the bowstring truss was in compression, like all arches, and so could be made of tough cast iron. Vertical rods of wrought iron ran from the arch to the flat roadway below. The pull of the roadway put them under tension, but this was eased by the cast iron diagonal members of the truss, which were in compression. It was a neat, clever way of spanning

A wooden bridge over Dale Creek built in 1868 of truss design, ideal for supporting the weight of a roadway across an abyss.

distances of 200 feet or less. And the Whipple bowstring truss could withstand the weight of the relatively light early railroad trains. Whipple himself noted that "steel has a greater power of resistance, but its cost precludes its use as a material for building."

Railroad Bridges

Thousands of these small truss bridges were built in the United States, and many of them are still to be seen. They left something to be desired, however, as railroad trains grew heavier. Newer and stronger iron truss bridges were devised. But the bridge-builders could not keep pace with the advances in railroad design. In 1831, the pride of the New York Central Railroad had been its locomotive, the *De Witt Clinton*, which weighed three and a half tons and traveled at the phenomenal speed of 20 miles an hour. A generation later, locomotives weighed 50 tons and more, and moved at 60 miles an hour. By 1880, even those locomotives seemed puny by comparison with the latest monstrous engines.

Railway bridges collapsed in startling regularity under these growing loads. The public took most of these disasters casually, calling them the price of progress, but the wreck of the Pacific Express on December 29, 1876, stirred wide protests. Two locomotives pulling eleven passenger cars plunged into a creek near Ashtabula, Ohio, when the iron bridge gave way. Eighty people were killed, the worst rail disaster America had ever seen. Other calamities followed. In the next 10 years, more than two hundred bridges collapsed. The wreck of a railway bridge at Chatsworth, Illinois, in 1887 produced a death toll greater than the Ashtabula wreck—84 lives. By then, cast iron was no longer being used for big bridges, but the old cast-iron bridges had not entirely been replaced.

The heavy new locomotives had pushed beyond the limits of cast iron's strength. Cast iron was too brittle, too likely to give way under an unexpected strain. The process of making cast iron often left serious hidden defects in the metal, besides. The bridge-builders hoped at first that wrought iron would be their salvation. Though much more expensive, wrought iron had four times the tensile strength of cast iron and could take compression nearly as well. A 515-foot bridge made entirely of wrought iron was placed across the Ohio River in 1876. But it was obsolete almost as soon as it was completed. The new 12-wheeled 80-ton locomotives, pounding along at 50 miles an hour, seriously taxed even the best wrought-iron bridges.

After a reign of less than a century, iron was finished as a structural material for large bridges. The time had come for the age of steel.

5:

Captain Eads
Builds A Bridge

Bridging the Mississippi in St. Louis

THE CITY OF ST. LOUIS, MISSOURI, HAD JUST 621 BUILDINGS AND 5,600 people when Missouri was admitted to the Union in 1821. To most Americans, it was an all-but-unknown outpost somewhere in the far West. But when steamboats began to ply the Mississippi, St. Louis' key position on the river turned it into a major port. By 1860, it had a population of 160,000, and a hundred big ships called there every week.

The river trade had made St. Louis wealthy. The city dominated north-south commerce in the heart of the continent. Railroads, too, saw the value of St. Louis' central position. From Chicago, the railroad capital of the nation, tracks ran westward toward St. Louis. But they could not reach the Missouri city, for the Mississippi, like a giant wall of water, cut St. Louis off from the eastern half of the nation.

A bridge was needed.

Bridging the Mississippi at St. Louis, though, was an assignment to make any engineer despair. The river was 1,500 feet wide. Its normal volume of flow past St. Louis was 225,000 cubic feet of water per second, but at the time of high water in June that flow was often quadrupled. The river could rise as high as 40 feet at flood time. At high water it shot past the city at twelve and a half feet per second. The bed of the river was a shifting layer of muck, with hard rock an unknown distance below it. An uncertain bottom, terrifying June floods, destructive icebergs careening down the river in winter—how could such a demon be bridged?

The people of St. Louis had no easy answers to that question. All they knew was that there had to be answers, for there had to be a bridge. The economic survival of the city depended on it.

The railways now ended in East St. Louis, a suburb across the river, and cargoes were ferried to the other side, weather permitting. From St. Louis, the Union Pacific Railroad ran westward to the developing frontier. A bridge across the river would put St. Louis right on the main railway line from one coast to the other. In the meanwhile, railroad men were beginning to bypass St. Louis entirely. In 1856, the Mississippi was bridged to the north at Rock Island, Illinois. The Rock Island Bridge, a five-span timber truss mounted on stone piers, was strong enough to carry a railroad from Illinois to Iowa and points west. The Union Pacific built a connecting line eastward toward Rock Island, and St. Louis watched unhappily as much profitable trade started to travel over this northern route. So long as St. Louis had nothing better to offer than a ferry, it stood to lose the east-west freight business to the Rock Island line. By 1866, the Missouri legislature had chartered the St. Louis and Illinois Bridge Company to span the gap, and the company looked about for an engineer who could build the impossible bridge. They found their man in Captain James Buchanan Eads.

Eads was born in 1820 and grew up in Kentucky, but when he was thirteen his family settled in booming St. Louis. Like Mark Twain and many another Missouri boy, young James Eads saw but one destiny for himself: life on the Mississippi. The vast river called to him. At nineteen, Eads landed a berth as a cargo clerk on a river steamboat. Three years later, he went into business for himself. Using self-taught engineering skills, he founded a company that specialized in salvaging wrecked steamboats. He invented clever derricks, pumps, and diving equipment, and located many old wrecks that contained salable cargoes. By 1856, the year that his cousin James Buchanan was elected President, Eads was the owner of ten salvage vessels.

Cousin James, as President, did not know how to handle the crisis of slavery that was splitting the nation apart. A few months after he turned the White House over to Abraham Lincoln in 1861, the country was locked in civil war. James Eads, now a wealthy man, began building ironclad ships for the Union. No one had ever built armored vessels before in America. (The *Monitor* and the *Merrimac*, which received most of the publicity, were simply the first ironclads to fight each other; they were built after Eads' ships.) The ingenuity of Captain Eads helped insure the Union's victory in the war. At the decisive Battle of Mobile Bay, two Eads ironclads led the attack that smashed the Confederate navy and opened the rivers to Union troops.

In all his varied endeavors, Eads had never built any bridges. The temptation to master the Mississippi was irresistible to him. Possibly because he was unfettered by past experience at bridge-building, Eads set out to build a bridge like none that had ever been constructed before—and succeeded.

That did not mean that he ignored the work of his predecessors. While planning his bridge, he went to Europe twice to find out what solutions other engineers had had for the classic problems of anchoring a foundation and supporting a roadway. Two challenges in particular faced Eads. He had to make his bridge strong enough to carry the most massive locomotives, which meant that even wrought iron would not be sufficient. And, since the site itself was so treacherous, he would have to drive his piers right to bedrock, which involved working at depths never before attempted.

He chose to build an arch bridge—the most rigid type. He would span the river with three consecutive arches, and he would fashion those arches from steel.

Steel was wrought iron carried to the next level of perfection. The brittleness of cast iron resulted from the impurities it contained, particularly carbon. Take the carbon out and wrought iron was produced. Put some of the carbon back in, under controlled conditions and high temperature, and a metal emerged that had

The Eads St. Louis Bridge over the Mississippi River, completed in 1874.

the strength of cast iron and the flexibility of wrought iron: steel. Swords of fine Damascus steel had been in demand for centuries. But steel was difficult to make, and existed only in small quantities. Until 1856, the idea of building a bridge from that rare, costly metal, steel, was as laughable as the idea of building one from gold or silver.

That was the year that Henry Bessemer hit upon his blast-furnace method for producing steel cheaply and in great quantities. Other advances followed, and by 1867, when Captain Eads began to design the St. Louis Bridge, dependable supplies of steel were available in quantities big enough for bridge-building purposes. Many engineers had no faith in the new metal, even so. In Great Britain, it was actually against the law until 1878 to use steel as a structural material for bridges. But James Eads was a law unto himself, and he proposed to build the world's first steel bridge.

Eads presented his design to the St. Louis and Illinois Bridge Company and it was accepted. Eads received the title of chief engineer. The Keystone Bridge Company of Pittsburgh, a leading bridge-building firm, was invited to construct the superstructure to Eads' design. J. H. Linville, a veteran engineer and the president of Keystone, looked at the plans and declared, "I cannot consent to imperil my reputation by appearing to encourage or approve [the design's] adoption. I deem it entirely unsafe and impracticable." He suggested an iron truss bridge instead. Eads, a persuasive talker, got the company's directors to ignore Linville's objections and proceed with the steel bridge as planned.

In August, 1867, Eads began construction of the cofferdam for the abutment on the western shore. Since there were to be three arches—a 520-foot center span flanked by two 502-foot spans—Eads had to build two piers in the deep water and an abutment near each shore. As an experienced salvage man, he knew the bottom well, and turned aside all suggestions to found the piers in the mud. "There is no safety short of resting the piers of your Bridge firmly on the rock itself," he wrote to the directors of the bridge company.

Downward through the mud of the shore went the piles of the western abutment. Tons of muck were cleared away, and solid masonry soon rose. The difficult part of the job lay ahead: the two mid-water piers, and the eastern abutment, which would have to be the deepest of all. In the fall of 1868 Eads went to Europe, partly to get away from St. Louis' damp, chilly winter while he recovered from a bronchial infection, and partly to talk to French engineers about the pneumatic caisson.

Caissons had come into use in the middle of the 19th century for construction jobs where an ordinary cofferdam would not suffice. A cofferdam is nothing more than a box, open at top and bottom, driven into the riverbed to create an enclosed area that can be pumped dry. Where the bed was of rock, cofferdam piles could not be driven. Where the foundation had to be unusually deep, a cofferdam would not reach far enough into the subsoil. Lastly, in deep work there was the problem of the water pressure, which grows more intense as the depth increases. At great depths, the pressure of the water would close like a giant fist around a cofferdam, crushing it.

Caissons were devised to cope with these difficulties. They, too, are boxes, but open only at the bottom. A partition ten feet or so above the bottom of the caisson creates an airtight working chamber. Above the roof of this chamber are shafts for various purposes: one for the workmen, one through which muck and debris can be carried, and one to admit compressed air. Constantly toiling pumps force compressed air into the working chamber. The air pressure must always balance the pressure of the water outside the caisson, or the caisson will collapse. At sea level, air pressure amounts to nearly 15 pounds per square inch—that is, the seemingly weightless air is actually exerting the weight of three or four encyclopedia volumes on every square inch of our bodies. (The air within our bodies is pressing outward just as strongly, which is why we aren't flattened.) Under water, the rapid increase of water pressure requires an equal increase in air pressure, so that at a depth of 120 feet, an air pressure of 52 pounds per square inch must be maintained to keep a caisson from being crushed.

Pneumatic caissons were first used in 1851 in England to construct the 61-foot-deep piers of the Rochester Bridge. The caisson, which had a sharp cutting edge at its open lower end, descended through the muck of the river bottom. Workmen in the open chamber at the bottom breathed compressed air as they shoveled the mud into buckets that were hauled up the muck shaft. At last, the caisson rested on the underlying rock bed, and could be filled with concrete and used as the foundation for the bridge pier. Other engineers had improved the design of the pneumatic caisson since that first effort. Eads talked with them and studied their methods. He returned to St. Louis to sink caissons deeper than had ever been done before.

Two caissons were constructed of wood sheathed in iron. These would serve for the two mid-water piers. The deep eastern abutment would require a caisson too, but the problems there were so immense that Eads preferred to gain experience by sinking the piers first. In October, 1869, the empty caisson of the east pier was towed to its site, two-thirds of the way from St. Louis to the Illinois shore. Testing had already revealed that bedrock lay under 82 feet of mud. The caisson was lowered until its cutting edges rested atop the mud. Workmen entered the nine-foot high chamber at the bottom and began shoveling away the mud, while a layer of brick-faced stone masonry was placed in the caisson above the roof of the working chamber.

As the weight of the masonry increased, the caisson was driven deeper and deeper into the river bottom. The pumps kept the air pressure steadily rising in the working chamber, always balancing the water pressure outside. The pressure rose to 20 pounds per square inch, 25, 30. It was winter, now, and the river churned with ice; but there were no seasons for the men who dug deep below the water. As the pressure rose, a few of the men complained of illness—stomach pains or a stiffness in the joints. Workers in other caisson jobs had had the same troubles, and had nicknamed the discomfort "the bends." It usually struck after they had finished work and returned to the upper world.

No one had any idea what caused the bends. The workmen shrugged them off as a hazard of their trade, and some of them wrapped strips of metal around their wrists and ankles in accordance with a fanciful theory for warding off the discomfort. Then, when the caisson was at a depth of 76 feet, with air pressure at 32 pounds, the first serious attack struck. A workman came to the surface, doubled over with abdominal pains, and had to be taken to a hospital. Eads decided that from then on no man would work longer than two hours at a stretch in the compressed air of the caisson, and allowed only his strongest men to go down at all.

That change appeared to be effective. In February, 1870, the caisson touched bedrock at 93½ feet. The working chamber was filled with masonry and the upper part of the caisson, which had been weighted but not completely filled, now received its stone load as well. The spring floods were starting, though. The water level rose around the fixed caisson, and the air pressure within it had to be increased as the final filling proceeded. A man named James Riley did his two-hour stint in the caisson at 44-pound pressure, came out in seemingly fine health, and fell dead ten minutes later. Five more deaths followed in a few days. Eads put his men under strict rules of diet and sleep, and cut the working day to three shifts of an hour at a time, with long rest periods between. The bends continued to strike, and the work shift had to be cut to 45 minutes. By April, the eastern pier was finished.

Work had proceeded simultaneously on the western pier. The caisson did not have to be sunk so deeply there, and the technical problems were fewer. Only one man had died of the bends during the construction of the western pier; twelve had perished on the eastern pier. Dozens of workers had been paralyzed. The cause of the caisson disease was still unknown, though obviously working under compressed air had something to do with it.

Eads, troubled by the 13 deaths and the many cases of paralysis, called in a doctor named Jaminet to keep his men in good health while the extremely difficult eastern abutment was constructed. Dr. Jaminet prescribed various rules for the men—plenty of rest and hot soup, short working hours in the caisson, and so forth. He did not strike the real remedy for the bends until he himself had suffered an agonizing seizure after returning from a visit to the caisson. The trouble, he guessed, lay in a too-sudden return from high pressure to normal pressure. He recommended that the men come up from the caisson slowly, so that the pressure about them would drop no faster than six pounds per minute.

Short working shifts under pressure, slow decompression—those were Dr. Jaminet's answers to the bends. They were the right answers. When the caisson of the eastern abutment reached a depth of 100 feet, he cut the working day to two shifts of 45 minutes each, and brought the men back carefully from below. There were still some cases of mild paralysis, but no deaths, until at 49 pounds one man was stricken. He died two weeks later—the only fatality on the eastern abutment.

Many years passed before the caisson disease was fully understood. In 1876, a French doctor discovered that men working under high pressure build up an excess of nitrogen in the tissues of the body. During decompression, the nitrogen gas is released as bubbles in the blood and tissues. Fast decompression releases these bubbles rapidly, causing pain in the joints and muscles, paralysis, or death.

Working short shifts helped to prevent the build-up of nitrogen; slow decompression allowed the nitrogen to be drained safely from the system without liberating the deadly bubbles. Dr. Jaminet's rate of decompression was much faster than that accepted today. A man working for four hours at a pressure of 40 pounds would spend 105 minutes in decompression. The development of the recompression chamber makes it unnecessary to remain at great depths during the decompression period. A man who has been exposed to pressure now returns fairly swiftly to the surface but is immediately placed in a recompression chamber that simulates the conditions below. Decompression can take place in relative comfort, under medical supervision if necessary, in such a chamber.

Lacking any of this knowledge, Eads and Dr. Jaminet did their best to keep their workmen from the mysterious disease. Despite the bends, floods, winter storms, and other obstacles, the caisson of the east abutment at last reached bedrock at the stupefying depth of 127½ feet. It was plugged with concrete and the masonry pier was constructed above it.

All four foundations of the bridge now were in place, after more than three years of toil. Of the 600 workmen, 14 had died and 119 had suffered serious paralysis; the price of Eads' amazing engineering feat had been high. The great piers rested on bedrock, though, capable of withstanding the fiercest rage of the Father of Waters. Eads had done the impossible. All that remained was the placing of the steel arches, which was merely improbable.

Getting the right quality of steel had kept Eads busy for several years. Steel was still something of a mystery metal, and the firms that had contracted to supply the steel for the bridge kept falling short of Eads' demands. He wanted a metal that was both strong and elastic, able to stand up under stress and to snap back to its original form afterward. His stubborn insistence on the highest quality left the steelmakers bewildered and angry as he rejected their efforts. Andrew Carnegie, the head of one of the companies making the steel for the bridge, was driven to complain, "Nothing that would and does please engineers is good enough for this work."

The proper quality of steel was eventually forthcoming,

though—at enormous cost. The bridge company was running millions of dollars over its initial budget, and had to go to the bankers for loans. Early in 1873, construction of the arches began. Eads could not build them in the usual fashion, by erecting a timber centering to hold the arches until they were self-supporting. To do that would mean blocking the entire river to shipping for more than a year. Instead, he supported the incomplete arches by tying them with strong steel cables to the piers. The cables descended from the tops of the two piers and two abutments, and held the unfinished arches in suspension as they reached out over the water.

Each of the three arch spans consisted of four steel ribs side by side, each rib made up of two parallel arched tubes a dozen feet apart, linked by diagonal bracing. As the arches grew, it became ever more exacting to keep them from ripping loose of their own weight. The steel cables that held them firm had to be constantly adjusted and extended. The job of keeping the growing arches supported went to a young engineer named Theodore Cooper, who nearly joined the list of the bridge's fatalities. Working on the arch one day, Cooper tripped and plunged into the river ninety feet below. As he fell, he curled his body into a tight ball to reduce the impact, and he landed unhurt. Half an hour later, after changing his clothes, he was back on the job. Now Cooper drove the men to complete the arches, and, as he told Eads later, "We were so sleepy that it was almost impossible to keep our eyes open and I was much afraid that some of us would fall into the river."

In September, 1873, the first arch was nearly complete. The two halves of the arch had been built toward each other all summer and a gap of only a few inches separated them. All that remained was the closing of the gap. Much depended on that small task, for Eads himself had gone to London to negotiate one more loan so that the bridge could be finished. The bankers had agreed to advance another $500,000, but only on the condition that the first arch be closed by September 19. If Eads missed the deadline, he would get no loan, and construction of the bridge would have to halt for months or even years while new financial support was obtained.

On September 14, five days before the deadline, the engineers attempted to close the arch. But a heat wave had unexpectedly hit St. Louis; the warmth had expanded the steel tubes of the arch, so that it was impossible to insert the piece that would close it. Racing against time, the bridge-builders packed tons of ice in wooden troughs around the arch. The ribs contracted as they cooled, and the space between the two sections of the arch widened until it was almost big enough to allow the last piece to be slipped into place. Almost. The gap was still five-eighths of an inch too narrow, and more ice failed to help. With two days remaining to the deadline, the engineers desperately resorted to tightening the ribs and jacking up the steel supporting cables, and this allowed them to slide a hastily-designed connecting joint into position. After 65 hours of round-the-clock work, the arch was closed.

One crisis remained. The following year, as work on the bridge neared completion, Eads was in New York arranging another loan when a telegram from Theodore Cooper arrived. The ribs of the arches, Cooper said, were splitting apart. Already, two tubes in the first span had cracked.

Eads guessed what the trouble was. Although the arches now were joined, the steel supporting cables had not yet been taken down. In the chilly winter weather, the cables were contracting, pulling the arch ribs upward. The arches were designed to bear compression, not tension. Eads wired Cooper to loosen the cables. While crowds gathered on the Mississippi shore expecting to see the great bridge tumble to destruction, the cables were removed. The arches held, self-supporting at last. The roadway was put in place, and on May 24, 1874, the bridge was officially opened to pedestrians. Several months of tests followed, the climax coming when on July 2 Eads corralled 14 locomotives, weighing 700 tons in all, and sent them across the bridge. Seven went across on each track, side by side, and the bridge held. Then all 14 made the journey in single file, like circus elephants on parade. Eads had hoped to borrow enough locomotives to line the entire bridge with them at once; but these 14, all that he could locate, were more than sufficient to prove the strength of his bridge. Two days later,

St. Louis held a gaudy Fourth of July celebration in which a procession of citizens 15 miles long paraded over the new bridge, while brass bands played and fireworks sparkled overhead.

The gleaming triple arch of James Eads' St. Louis Bridge was hailed rightfully as an engineering landmark. It was the biggest bridge that had ever been built at that time, the first steel bridge, and, in fact, the first large work of any kind in steel. Eads' use of pneumatic caissons for the foundations had been another trailblazing accomplishment, for no one had ever worked at such a depth. The St. Louis Bridge, which is still in use, transformed St. Louis into an important rail center and gave James Eads an immortal rank among great engineers.

The same year that Eads began his bridge, another historic bridge was taking form to the east. It also was a steel bridge. But it had little else in common with the bridge of Captain Eads. The Brooklyn Bridge was as different from the St. Louis Bridge as a bridge could be—yet it, too, was a monument of enduring greatness.

6:

Roebling & Son, Engineers

NEW YORK IS A CITY OF ISLANDS. ONLY ONE OF ITS FIVE BOROUGHS—
the Bronx—is actually on the mainland of North America. Brooklyn
and Queens occupy the western tip of huge Long Island; Manhattan, the hub of the city, is completely surrounded by water, and
so, of course, is the fifth borough, Staten Island. The waterways
that separate the boroughs of New York are large ones. The East
River, which divides Manhattan from Long Island, is 1,600 feet
wide in some places, about as wide as the Mississippi is at St.
Louis. The Hudson River, which cuts New York off from the rest
of the country, is much wider. Even the bays and inlets that sub-
divide the city are sizable. Such a city, if it is to maintain its unity,
demands great bridges. And New York has received bridges to
match its greatness. No other city in the world has so many bridges
of such size and power. An afternoon of driving through New York
amounts to a tour through the history of bridge-building, for every
type of bridge can be seen in the city, including at least four that
are internationally famous.

A century ago, this was not the case. Ferries were the only
form of contact between the islands that make up New York.
Getting from Manhattan to Brooklyn was a major journey. Brooklyn was then an independent city, and to many Manhattanites it

must have seemed like an unknown world. Many New Yorkers had visited London and Paris a dozen times but had never set foot in Brooklyn.

The proud people of Brooklyn were troubled by this. They felt the need to join themselves to Manhattan by something more efficient than a ferry, since the ferries were often shut down for weeks on end during severe winters. Many Brooklynites worked in Manhattan, then as now the commercial and financial heart of the city. Political leaders in Brooklyn called for the building of a bridge, and in the middle of the 19th century the New York Bridge Company was organized for the purpose of ending the isolation of the borough. In 1857, a remarkable engineer named John Roebling proposed a suspension bridge crossing from Brooklyn to the lower end of Manhattan near City Hall. After a decade of debate, he got the job, and produced a revolutionary structure that is the classic of its kind.

Suspension bridges were not in high favor when John Roebling began his career. The only really successful large-scale suspension bridge of the time had been Telford's Menai Strait Bridge of the 1820's, and even that had had its problems. Others had blown down with dreary regularity in Europe. A suspension bridge might be fine for short spans, but not for anything of much size. Such bridges were too flimsy, too unreliable; their dangling roadbeds whipped about wildly in storms, or gave way beneath the strain of carrying heavy loads. Certainly in an age of big locomotives a large bridge had to be rigid and unyielding. No form could be less yielding than an arch, which was why James Eads used that design for his bridge at St. Louis. John Roebling, however, set out to prove that a suspension bridge just as enduring as any arch bridge could be built.

In theory, suspension bridges had great advantages. They required less material than arch bridges and could attain longer spans. Even today, it is impossible to build an arch bridge with a span greater than 2,500 feet, because of the inherent problems of the form; a longer span would be too heavy to support its own weight. A suspension bridge, lighter and more flexible, can nearly double that limit. As early as 1867 John Roebling was speaking quite seriously about suspension bridges with 3,000-foot spans, while the current record-holder, the Verrazano-Narrows Bridge in New York, has a span of 4,260 feet.

But such spans seemed like idle dreams to most engineers of the era. They clung to the tried and tested arch bridge. A few experimenters dabbled with suspension bridges; a French engineer worked out a method for spinning wire into cable at the bridge site, directly on the suspension towers, and a British engineer suggested that the roadways of such bridges could be braced against the wind with stiffening trusses. No one took a chance on building a major suspension bridge, though. One failure could ruin an engineer's career.

John Roebling, a big, hulking man with shaggy eyebrows and a grim, fierce expression, was willing to take that chance, because he was confident of success. Roebling came to America in 1831, at the age of twenty-five, after studying engineering in his native Germany. For six years he supported himself by farm labor in Pennsylvania while continuing his engineering studies; then he became a canal engineer, and gradually moved into bridge work. When fire destroyed a Pittsburgh bridge in the 1840's, Roebling won the contract to rebuild it. He did the job for $55,000—a startlingly low cost. The secret of economy was the suspension form. His roadway, stiffened by trusses, was sturdy and solid, and won him great praise.

Niagara Bridge

In 1848, a flamboyant character named Charles Ellet received a contract to bridge the gorge of the Niagara River near the famous waterfall. Ellet, a cocky promoter who teemed with grandiose ideas, had built the first wire-cable suspension bridge in America seven years before, at Philadelphia. He had also proposed a suspension bridge at St. Louis with a span of 6,500 feet, something that would be deemed fantastic today and certainly was impossible then; he did not get the job. Ellet and Roebling had competed for the Niagara assignment, and Ellet was picked.

To build a suspension bridge, a temporary working platform must be stretched from tower to tower. That involves stringing cables across a gaping gorge, which is generally achieved by send-ing a boat across the gorge carrying an initial cable that can be hoisted into place. At Niagara, though, foaming rapids made such a boat trip impossible. Ellet solved the problem by offering five dollars to any boy who could fly a kite across the gorge and tie its string to a tree on the other side. A boy named Homan Walsh won the reward, helped by a friend who caught the kite and fastened it. Now a string stretched from shore to shore, high above the rushing river, and Ellet's engineers used this to carry their first cables. Soon several iron cables were in place. Ellet fastened a basket to the cables, climbed into it, and pulled himself across—the first man ever to cross Niagara's gorge.

A few weeks later a temporary bridge seven and a half feet wide spanned the gorge, 240 feet above the river. To demonstrate its safety, Ellet crossed it on horseback. The little bridge was in-tended as a working space for the men who would build the final span, but before Ellet could proceed he found himself in a quarrel with his backers over payment. He quit in anger, and John Roeb-ling was called in to finish the job.

While Roebling was at work on the Niagara Bridge, word came that another Ellet suspension bridge in West Virginia had collapsed in a storm. This bridge, at Wheeling, had a thousand-foot span, the longest in the world at that time. An account in the New York *Times* told of the destruction of the roadway: "At one time it rose to nearly the height of the tower, then fell, and twisted and writhed, and was dashed almost bottom upward. At last there seemed to be a determined twist along the entire span, about one half of the flooring being nearly reversed, and down went the immense structure from its dizzy height to the stream below, with an appalling crash and roar."

Roebling understood why the Wheeling Bridge had fallen—not because its suspension cables were too weak to hold it up, but because its roadway had been too flexible. "That bridge," he wrote, "was destroyed by the momentum acquired by its own dead weight, when swayed up and down by the force of the wind. . . . The destruction of the Wheeling Bridge was clearly owing to a want of stability, and not to a want of strength. This want of stiffness could have been supplied by over-floor stays, truss railings, under-floor stays, or cable stays."

Still convinced of the basic merits of the suspension idea, Roebling took immediate steps to stiffen his Niagara structure, adding a heavy timber truss between the two decks of its roadway. In 1855 the bridge was finished—an 820-foot span supported by four wrought-iron cables 10 inches in diameter. The first test was triumphant. Roebling reported: "With an engine of 28 tons we pushed over from Canada to New York twenty double-loaded freight cars making a gross weight of 368 tons; this train very nearly covered the whole length of floor between the towers. . . . No vibrations whatever."

Roebling's Niagara Bridge was a success. In 1881 the wooden roadway was replaced by an iron one, and four years after that the original stone towers were supplanted by towers of steel, but the suspension idea itself was vindicated even though the parts of the bridge themselves were reconstructed. The growth of Niagara traffic brought about the dismantling of the bridge in 1897, when a larger one was constructed.

Roebling's experience at Niagara led him to new suspension projects at Pittsburgh and at Cincinnati. One of the engineers who assisted him on these bridges was a young man named Washington Roebling, who had just graduated from Rensselaer Polytechnic Institute. They formed an outstanding father-and-son team until the outbreak of the Civil War, when the younger Roebling enlisted in the Union army.

Before the war, Washington Roebling had been in charge of the work at Pittsburgh, supervising the construction to his father's design. The Cincinnati Bridge, which was delayed by financial and engineering problems, was incomplete when Washington went off to war; but in January, 1865, with the Union victory all but certain, Colonel Washington Roebling resigned from the army and went to Cincinnati to see the bridge through. Its towers were soon completed and the 1,057-foot span of the roadway, a record length, followed quickly.

The Roeblings had built the three longest suspension bridges in the country, and all three had been outstandingly successful.

When in 1867 John Roebling took on the Brooklyn-New York assignment, he now proposed to build a bridge with a 1,600-foot suspended span, half again as large as the new Cincinnati giant. The promoters of the bridge were themselves taken aback by the grandeur of Roebling's plan. With sublime confidence bordering on arrogance, Roebling informed them, "The contemplated work, when constructed in accordance with my designs, will not only be the greatest bridge in existence, but it will be the great engineering work of this Continent and of the age."

Brooklyn Bridge

Two years passed before the objections of the cautious could be overcome. City and government officials gave their approval at last, and in the summer of 1869 John Roebling began surveying the site of the bridge that would crown his memorable career. On a July morning, standing on a ferry slip at the Brooklyn waterfront, Roebling was taking measurements when a ferryboat made a clumsy approach and crashed into the slip. Roebling's foot was caught and crushed; an infection set in, and doctors were unable to halt its spread. In two weeks he was dead, and the bridge that was to have been his masterpiece became his monument instead.

Washington Roebling, thirty-two years old and himself an experienced engineer, took his father's place. Perhaps only a man cast in the same heroic mold as John Roebling could have seen the Brooklyn Bridge through to completion. The great span, the depth of the river, the decision to use the unfamiliar "metal of the future," steel, for the cables—all these made the job a titanic challenge. John Roebling had used·iron for the cables of his earlier suspension bridges, but he had said as early as 1855, "By substituting the best quality of steel wire, we may nearly double the span and afford the same degree of security." A suspension bridge the size of this one could be supported only by steel; but no one had used steel cable this way before.

Another steel bridge was already under construction, the Eads bridge in St. Louis, but that was to be an arch bridge. In 1870 Washington Roebling made a trip to St. Louis to confer with Eads. He wished to observe Eads' use of pneumatic caissons, not Eads' use of steel, for the St. Louis Bridge was a long way from the construction of its superstructure.

Roebling's caissons did not have to go as deep as Eads', but there were other problems to be met. Instead of soft mud, Roebling had to drive his caissons into a rocklike clay called "hard pan," which had to be blasted loose from the floor of the East River. In March, 1870, the Brooklyn caisson began to descend. The work was uneventful though taxing at first. One Sunday, when by good fortune no work was in progress, the caisson suffered a "blowout"—a mishap caused by a compressed-air leak in one of the caisson shafts. With a whooshing roar, the compressed air escaped from the caisson and went rocketing to the surface, sending mud and water 500 feet into the air and astounding the people of Brooklyn, whose houses were spattered for blocks around with particles of river muck. Three watchmen who happened to be on the caisson at the time were badly shaken up, but not injured seriously, and the caisson itself miraculously remained unharmed. A similar caisson blowout in Russia a few years later would take 29 lives.

The caisson was filled again with compressed air and work resumed. The editor of a contemporary magazine paid a visit, and wrote his description of the activities in the working chamber on the river floor:

"This work of excavation is very simple, albeit very hard for the laborers. . . . The bed of the excavation is slush and mud, slowly carried by shoveling to the apparatus by which it is removed. Numerous large boulders are met with, and are drilled and broken to fragments before being taken out. Small calcium lights throw steaming luminous jets into the corners where the workmen are busy. . . . The mud and silt under foot, the dank wooden walls at the sides, the chambers dim in the scattered lights, and the laborers moving like good-natured gnomes in the shadows, complete the picture."

Because the river bottom was so hard, the caisson went down at a rate of six inches a week. The risky process of blasting within the caisson sped things up, but introduced the danger of fire. Several times, the beams of the caisson caught fire, but these were quickly extinguished. Roebling's workmen—360 of them, toiling continuously in three shifts of eight hours each—drove the caisson ever deeper into the bottom. But in December, 1870, a serious fire inside the caisson threatened to halt everything. The thick timber roof of the working chamber caught fire and burned for several hours before anything was noticed. The blaze burned channels, outwardly invisible but potentially dangerous, deep within the mass of wood. Since the entire weight of the caisson's masonry filling had to rest on this wooden partition, any unseen structural defect jeopardized the safety of the entire bridge.

When the fire was discovered, Washington Roebling spent all night leading the struggle to put it out. By dawn, the blaze seemed under control. But the exhausted Roebling ordered exploratory holes drilled deep into the timbering, and found that at a depth of four feet the fire still smouldered. He decided on a bold and dangerous step: flooding the caisson. Air pressure was lowered and the water rushed in. For two and a half days the interior of the caisson was allowed to soak, before the pumps began pushing the water out again. The fire was dead; but the timber partition was honeycombed with charred passages, and liquid cement had to be forced into them to insure the strength of the caisson.

There were other misadventures, but finally the Brooklyn caisson reached bedrock at 44½ feet, and by May, 1872, served as the foundation for a masonry tower that stood 75 feet above the river. Meanwhile, the much more difficult task of lowering the caisson on the New York side was proceeding.

Bedrock here was 78 feet down. That was not so deep as Eads' foundations, but it was deep enough to introduce the problem of caisson disease, which had not caused difficulties on the Brooklyn side. The upper levels of the river bottom had served for years as a garbage dump, and the men were plagued by the unbearable stench; but soon they were through the garbage layer and were facing a much grimmer adversary: the bends. Working at a pressure of 35 pounds per square inch, the men began to collapse as they reached the surface. The first death occurred in April, 1872. Two more followed, and a hundred workers were hospitalized. Eads had already been through this nightmare in St. Louis, and

Dr. Jaminet had worked out limits on work shifts and on decompression time that had helped to reduce, though not to eliminate entirely, cases of the disease. None of Eads' valuable experience came to the ears of Colonel Roebling, however, and the men at work in the East River relied on the useless health rules of the time—plenty of sleep, good diet, warm clothing—which had nothing to do with the fateful nitrogen bubbles that were paralyzing them. If the Brooklyn Bridge's caissons had had to go down to the 127½-foot depth of Eads' eastern abutment, there might have been dozens of deaths. As it was, the toll was high.

Among the victims was Washington Roebling. The giant 53,000-ton New York caisson was in place and nearly filled with concrete when an emergency developed. Roebling went down into the caisson and spent 12 consecutive hours under compressed air. When he came out, he collapsed in terrible pain, crippled with paralysis. He was unable to return to the job. Now a helpless invalid, he withdrew to his apartment on Columbia Heights, overlooking the Brooklyn side of the bridge. When his strength returned, he directed the construction by remote control, watching with field glasses from his bed and relaying his orders via his wife. Unable to leave his room, the stricken engineer nevertheless refused to relinquish command of his mighty enterprise.

The towers now were rising above the caisson foundations. By June, 1875, the Brooklyn pier was complete, and the New York pier was finished 13 months later. On shore behind each pier stood huge anchorage blocks containing the metal plates to which the bridge cables would be fastened. In the summer of 1876, the spinning of the cables began—the most dramatic and fascinating part of erecting a suspension bridge.

Old John Roebling had not invented the cable-spinning technique, but he had brought it to perfection, and his son now saw it employed for the first time with steel. First a temporary catwalk had to be erected. No kites were flown this time. On an August morning a scow was towed across the river, trailing a cable that was allowed to sink to the bottom. The cable was fastened to the anchorage at the Brooklyn side and was draped over the top of the Brooklyn tower. When the scow reached the New York side,

The Brooklyn Bridge, opened in 1883, was the first suspension bridge to use steel cables.

the cable was similarly draped over the tower there, and then fastened to a hoisting engine. A cannon was fired to warn ships to keep back, and the cable was hoisted, quickly breaking the surface and rising until it dangled from tower to tower high above the river. Other cables followed, and soon a flexible footbridge was in place.

Hundreds of huge reels of steel wire began to arrive at the anchorage points. The wire, about a fifth of an inch thick, had been made to unusual Roebling specifications: a strength of 160,000 pounds per square inch, twice as tough as the iron wire used in John Roebling's three great suspension bridges. The reels were hoisted to the tops of the anchorages, and the free end of each wire was attached to a large grooved pulley called a "traveling wheel." The traveling wheel swung out along the footbridge, rising to the top of the Brooklyn tower, then descending in a great sweep following the curve of the design, rising again to go over the New York tower, and coming to rest at the anchorage on the far shore. There, the wire was taken from the wheel and made fast to the anchorage, while the wheel made its return trip carrying another ribbon of steel to the other side.

Back and forth across the river the traveling wheels hummed. Every 286 wires were bound together by a steel wrapping to form a "strand." Nineteen strands, in turn, were bound together to make up a single cable. Each cable, nearly 16 inches in diameter, thus contained almost 5,500 wires. They were squeezed together by machine and surrounded by a metal skin. Four cables were fashioned altogether, each securely anchored on shore behind each tower. There was one spectacular accident while a strand was being anchored on the New York side; it broke loose, killing two men as it sprang into the air like a vicious serpent, and leaped 900 feet into the work yard under the New York tower. There it lay only a moment. The tension of the middle section of the strand, sagging between the two towers, whipped it into the air again, up and over the tower and into the river. It slashed the water only a short distance from a crowded ferryboat.

The traveling wheels made their thousands of round-trip journeys, and at length the four thick cables hung in a perfect curve from anchorage to anchorage, from tower to tower. The roadway now could be put in place, section by section. Working outward from the shore, the men constructed the steel roadway and fastened it by steel "hangers" to the four cables. The cables bore the weight of the roadway, transmitting it to the two towers. Tension was distributed through the cables and their anchorages and through the towers, and according to Washington Roebling's calculations the bridge would be strong enough to withstand a weight four times as great as any it would ever be expected to carry.

Though the bridge looked suspiciously flimsy to some observers accustomed to massive arch bridges, Roebling had actually taken every precaution to insure its strength. Sturdy steel trusses stiffened the roadway, making the floor rigid enough to carry the heaviest locomotive anyone could imagine. For extra safety, he ran diagonal "wind stays" from the roadway to the tops of the towers, giving the bridge a curious weblike appearance not seen on most later suspension bridges.

In 1883, the bridge was opened after 14 years of construction. It had cost some $13,000,000, had taken the lives of many workers, had sent John Roebling to his grave and had made a permanent invalid of his son. But now a web of steel bound Brooklyn and Manhattan together. The Roeblings had shown the way toward even more phenomenal steel suspension bridges, and in the future the Brooklyn Bridge would serve as the model for such titans as the George Washington Bridge, the Golden Gate Bridge, and the Verrazano-Narrows Bridge. Beside them, the bridge of the Roeblings would seem puny, yet every bridge-builder looks with reverence on that pioneering effort.

At the dedication ceremony in 1883, a New York Congressman named Abram Hewitt invited his listeners to "turn to the Bridge. It looks like a motionless mass of masonry and metal; but, as a matter of fact, it is instinct with motion. There is not a particle of matter in it which is at rest for the minutest portion of time. It is an aggregation of unstable elements, changing with every change in the temperature, and every movement of the heavenly bodies. The problem was, out of these unstable elements, to produce absolute stability; and it was this problem which the engineers, the organized intelligence, had to solve, or confess to inglorious failure. The problem has been solved."

More than any other, the man who solved that problem was Washington Roebling. Struck down in young manhood by the caisson disease, Roebling lived on to see horse-drawn carriages and then automobiles by the thousands go streaming across his bridge. He saw Brooklyn and Manhattan united to form the City of New York, a political alignment that served as the symbol of the union his work had forged. His two younger brothers took charge of the engineering firm that his father had founded, and built it to imposing size in the decades that followed. The crippled Colonel Roebling outlived them both. His strength slowly returned, and when his brothers died just after World War I he took charge of the firm—at the age of eighty-four. The powerful spirit within the injured body would not let go of life until 1926. Washington Roebling died on the eve of his ninetieth birthday. To the builders of bridges, he and his father stand with the immortals.

7:

New Bridges
For A New Century

A HUNDRED YEARS OF DYNAMIC PROGRESS HAD ENTIRELY TRANSFORMED the art of building bridges. Until the late 18th century there had really been only one basic form a large bridge could take: the arch. There was only one durable building material: stone. Architects might experiment with longer spans and thinner piers, but those were minor variations on a single theme.

A century later there were new materials, new techniques, new ideas. The use of iron and then steel had allowed bridges to grow to incredible dimensions. The bold gambles of John Roebling had established the suspension bridge as an acceptable means of spanning great gulfs. The equally venturesome James Eads had shown the virtues of the steel arch. Even the simple truss bridge flowered into many forms now that structural steel was available. As the new century opened, engineers had a wide range of basic bridge designs that could be adapted to fit the special needs of a particular site.

Cantilever Bridges

One of the new styles was the cantilever bridge, a variation on the oldest kind of bridge of all—the beam or girder bridge. As we saw in the first chapter, a log or a stone slab placed across a stream is a simple beam bridge. Its weight thrusts vertically against the ground along its entire length.

Support that flat horizontal beam on one or more piers, and it becomes a cantilever bridge. A cantilever is a balanced structure that juts out in two directions from its base or pier. The thrust of an arch is against the abutments at its sides; the pull of a suspension bridge is against its towers and anchorages; the thrust of a cantilever bridge is downward against its supporting piers. A single pier is enough to carry a short cantilever. For greater distances, two cantilevers could be placed end to end, or even more.

Though the cantilever idea is an ancient one, the first big cantilever bridges were constructed in the late 19th century. A catastrophe helped to bring the first one into being.

Two sharp inlets, the Firth of Forth and the Firth of Tay, cut deep into the eastern coast of Scotland. They lie between the important cities of Edinburgh and Dundee, and though those cities are only 46 miles apart, travelers could go from one to the other in the 19th century only by taking a double ferry journey lasting many hours. When railroads reached Scotland, the hope arose that the two firths could be bridged, permitting quick and easy contact between the two cities.

The Firth of Tay, near Dundee, was the first to be bridged. An engineer named Thomas Bouch designed a bridge over two miles long, consisting of a great many short spans. There were 85 wrought-iron trusses, 200 to 285 feet long, standing on cast-iron columns that rose from piers of brick and concrete. The bridge was completed in 1877, at a time when steel was still prohibited by law on British bridges.

Of the Tay Bridge's 85 spans, 72 had the supporting trusses below the roadway. In the middle of the firth, though, was a navigation channel for big ships, and to avoid interference with the smokestacks of these ships, the trusses of the center spans were placed above the roadway. These spans, 13 in number, were nicknamed "the High Girders." The sinister implications of that superstition-haunted number were overlooked. So, too, was the fact that the High Girders were poorly joined to the low-lying trusses on either side of them.

The Tay Bridge Disaster: Steam launches and divers' barge employed in search (December, 1879).

The bridge passed its first inspections and was opened for railroad traffic in 1878. Soon after, it was discovered that high winds in the firth had a tendency to loosen the wrought-iron cross-bracing between some of the piers. The bracing was strengthened, but no major repairs were carried out. A few engineers warned that the bridge was unstable.

On a Sunday late in December, 1879, a fierce winter gale struck Dundee. The storm still raged at 7:12 that evening when a train bound for Dundee rolled out onto the bridge. The signalmen at the southern end of the bridge watched the train go by, and then were dismayed to see its tail lights disappear. In horror they crawled out along the bridge in the howling gale until they could go no further. The 13 High Girders—and the train—were gone. The naked stumps of the piers alone remained. Seventy-five people had perished; there were no survivors.

The inquiry that followed the disaster produced many theories about the fall of the center spans. The high winds, the relative weakness of wrought iron, the flimsiness of the joints connecting the spans—all these contributed in some measure to the collapse. One member of the investigating commission bluntly declared, "This bridge was badly designed, badly constructed, and badly maintained. . . . Its downfall was due to inherent defects in the structure which must sooner or later have brought it down. Sir Thomas Bouch is, in our opinion, mainly to blame."

The career of the unhappy Bouch was destroyed. He had hoped to win the assignment to build the companion bridge over the Firth of Forth. Ruined by the inquiry, he broke down in health and soon was dead. In a short time a new Tay Bridge was under construction on new piers sixty feet west of the fallen bridge. Though also of iron, the new bridge was twice as heavy as its predecessor, to reassure a frightened public. Actually, the second Tay Bridge was made stronger than any bridge needed to be. It is still in use.

When the bridge-builders turned next to the Forth Bridge project, they were faced with the same need to win public confidence by building an over-safe bridge. The Firth of Forth provided some special engineering problems as well.

The Firth of Tay is wide but shallow. Its deepest point is only about 80 feet deep, so it was possible to use pneumatic caissons to lay the foundations of the piers. The Firth of Forth is more than twice as deep—as much as 218 feet in its north channel. Working at such depths would have called for an air pressure in the caisson of about 80 pounds per square inch, beyond the limits of toleration.

However, an island lies in the middle of the strait. The ill-fated Thomas Bouch had calculated that the central pier of a three-pier bridge could be placed on the flank of this island. So that the other two piers would rest in relatively shallow water, the spans of the bridge would have to be 1,600 feet long. Since the Brooklyn Bridge's span was that size, Bouch saw no reason why he could not build such a double suspension bridge across the Firth of Forth—even though he planned to use iron cables, and the Roeblings had used steel.

When the Tay Bridge collapsed, so did any chance of a suspension bridge for the Firth of Forth. If Bouch had suggested it, that was reason enough to reject the idea. In 1881, a cantilever design proposed by the engineer John Fowler and his young assistant Benjamin Baker was accepted. They borrowed the idea from a German bridge-builder named Heinrich Gerber, who had built a small cantilever bridge a few years before. Gerber in turn had been inspired by certain ancient timber bridges of China in the cantilever mode.

The Fowler-Baker idea coped with the difficulties of the site, while at the same time offering a bridge more likely to satisfy a jittery public than a suspension bridge. There were three main piers, one on the central island and the other two on the shores of the firth. From each of these piers two 680-foot cantilever arms jutted. The ends of these arms did not meet; there was a 350-foot gap between the end of one arm and the next, and across this gap a small suspended span was hung. The suspended span was supported not by piers but by the strength of the cantilever arms.

There were thus three spans in all. From north to south there was the 680-foot approach cantilever, the north pier, the next 680-foot cantilever, a 350-foot suspension span, another cantilever, the central pier, the fourth cantilever, the second suspension span, the fifth cantilever, the south pier, and the final cantilever leading onto land. Though it sounds so complicated as to carry great risks, Fowler and Baker saw to it that there was nothing fragile about this collection of cantilever arms and suspended spans. James Eads' St. Louis Bridge had required 11,000 tons of iron and steel; the Forth Bridge took 58,000 tons of steel. Its cantilevers were braced by monstrous trusses forming a vast spiderweb of metal. Over the piers, the trusses were 350 feet high, though they tapered to a mere 50-foot height at the suspended spans. The impression was one of immense weight and massiveness. Cradled in these colossal struts of steel, the Forth Bridge is one of the ugliest ever built, but also one of the strongest.

No chances were taken with the foundations, either. The piers on which the cantilevers rose were driven to bedrock, as deep as 88 feet. There were few cases of the bends, though some delay in the work resulted when a caisson capsized and had to be pumped dry and floated out of the mud in which it had settled. During the building of the massive superstructure, 57 lives were lost. The complex trusses of the cantilevers were built outward from the piers, piece by piece, and many fatal accidents stemmed from carelessness: men killed by hammers dropped from higher levels of the bridge, and so on. When the time came to close the first span, a problem developed opposite to that of the St. Louis Bridge; unusually cold weather caused the metal to contract so the arms would not meet, and a fire had to be lit along the steelwork so that the last sections could be linked.

The Forth Bridge was an engineering success, though something less than a work of art. It established the cantilever bridge as a rival of the suspension bridge for long-span situations. Some engineers, eyeing the giant trusses of the cantilever form, regarded it as a safer and more stable structure than a suspension. Soon after the turn of the new century, a second East River bridge was constructed just north of the Brooklyn Bridge, and though this was a suspension bridge it made use of heavy trusses. This was the Williamsburg Bridge, whose 40-foot stiffening trusses gave it the cluttered look of a cantilever.

The next East River bridge was a true cantilever. It was the Queensboro Bridge, built several miles north of the Williamsburg. Intended to carry subway trains from midtown Manhattan to the Borough of Queens, this bridge had to be extremely strong, and— despite the evidence of the Brooklyn Bridge—the engineers of that day preferred to rely on the theoretically stronger cantilever design, rather than a suspension.

As at the Firth of Forth, an island in mid-channel provided a foundation for the central pier. There were no suspended spans in the Queensboro Bridge, though; the cantilever arms met end to end. The island was flanked by two piers carrying a 630-foot span, which joined with two equal cantilever arms of 1,182 feet each over the channels of the river. The bridge looks something like a suspension bridge, until one notices that its roadway is supported by piers and does not hang from cables. When the bridge was finished, it turned out to be an engineer's horror; despite its strong foundations and the use of 50,000 tons of steel, it was not sturdy enough to carry the intended load. The continuous series of cantilever arms happened to have curious properties. For all the ponderousness of the bridge, it was just barely able to carry its own dead load. Two of the four subway tracks had to be shifted to a tunnel under the river. Neither beautiful nor fully effective, the Queensboro Bridge made New York's engineers wish they had had more confidence in the suspension form that the Roeblings had perfected. Most of the later big bridges in New York were of the suspension type.

The brief but widespread popularity of the cantilever bridge at the turn of the century produced a different kind of engineering

The Queensboro Bridge was built as a true cantilever because engineers of that day believed it stronger than the suspension design.

nightmare in Canada. In 1904, work began on a bridge across the St. Lawrence River in Quebec—a colossal cantilever, with a main span of 1,800 feet. Patterned somewhat after the Forth Bridge, the Quebec Bridge would have the longest single span in the world.

Theodore Cooper of New York served as the consulting engineer who planned the bridge. Thirty years earlier, Cooper had been James Eads' assistant in St. Louis; Cooper was the one who had survived a fall from the bridge and returned almost at once to the job. Now he was nearly seventy, an invalid who could not leave New York. He had become America's most famous bridge engineer since the retirement of Washington Roebling, and he was often asked to give his advice on new constructions.

The Quebec Bridge was to have only two piers, one on each shore. The giant cantilever arms would be built on the shoreward side first, and temporarily supported by props known as "falsework." Next, the inner arms would be built toward each other over the water. When they were complete, a suspended span would be added to join them, temporarily supported by cables from above, as had been done during the construction of the arches of the St. Louis Bridge.

By the summer of 1907, the shoreward and riverward spans of the south cantilever were finished and the southern half of the suspended span was edging outward across the river. One day it was discovered that the incomplete suspended span had dipped a fraction of an inch toward the water. Word was sent to Cooper in New York. He recognized the danger of the situation: obviously the ribs of the cantilever arm, which would be strong enough to support the suspended span when it was finished, were weakening under the strain of holding the incomplete span erect. Cooper replied that the engineers at the site should study methods of bracing the span.

He made the natural assumption that they would halt all work on the bridge while planning ways to strengthen the construction area. Instead, the engineers let work proceed. While they pondered the support problem, a heavy crane was allowed to move out onto the next panel of the suspended span. The span dipped

The Quebec Bridge joins two shores of the St. Lawrence River near Quebec City.

another inch. Cooper was aghast when he learned that work had continued. He sent a telegram to Quebec, demanding an instant halt. It was too late. Before it could arrive, the unfinished span and the entire south cantilever arm ripped loose. Into the St. Lawrence went 9,000 tons of steel and 86 workmen. Only 11 men survived.

It was the worst bridge construction disaster in history, both in terms of cost and lives lost. Much of the blame went to Theodore Cooper, since he was the one who had planned the original unsafe design. But Cooper had realized the flaws in his plan in time to avoid loss of life, and if he had been on the scene the catastrophe would not have occurred. The failure of the Quebec engineers to use common sense had destroyed the bridge and killed 75 men.

The Quebec authorities scrapped the Cooper design and ordered a new bridge—again of the cantilever type. It took two years to clear the wreckage of the first bridge from the water. The steel-work that had not fallen had to be demolished. Not even the piers of the Cooper bridge could be used. New piers, 65 feet south of the original ones, were built. The most modern medical treatment was employed to deal with caisson disease, and there were no fatal-ities from the bends. By 1914, the new foundations were in place. Within two years, the cantilever arms were complete. All that re-mained was to insert the 640-foot-long suspended span.

The designers of the new bridge had wished to avoid the need to build the middle span out from the two arms. Instead, they con-structed the span on the riverbank and planned to use enormous cranes to lift it into position. In September, 1916, barges floated the span to mid-river and the cranes began to raise it. As it rose, it was fastened by links to the waiting cantilever arms. It was nearly in place when one of the links snapped. The 5,000-ton span tilted, crumpled, and plunged into the river. Thirteen men were killed. The jinxed bridge went unfinished for another year while a new span was built. This time, it was successfully put in place and the bridge opened in 1918.

The Quebec Bridge is still the longest-span cantilever bridge in the world, ahead of the Forth Bridge and the Hooghly Bridge in Calcutta, completed in 1943. A number of shorter cantilever bridges have been constructed, but the style has lost favor among engineers. The Tay calamity spurred the initial popularity of canti-lever bridges; the Quebec disaster 40 years later helped bring that popularity to an end.

Steel Arch Bridges

The Eads bridge at St. Louis had a dramatic impact on the fortunes of the arch style. Once the glamorous captain had blazed the path, other engineers produced steel arch bridges that far ex-ceeded the model. In the general ferment of new engineering ideas at the close of the 19th century, the hinged arch design appeared and made possible bigger and better steel arches.

The hinged arch's ends rest on huge steel wheels called "rolling pins," several feet in diameter. These pins deal with the tendency of a metal arch to bend under a heavy load by introducing a certain degree of "give," so that the arch can change its angle of curvature slightly. Usually one pin was placed at each end of the arch, forming what became known as a "two-hinged arch." The "three-hinged arch" had an additional pin at the top, where the two halves of the arch met. The "one-hinged arch" simply had the top pin.

Steel arches attained great popularity among European engineers. Gustave Eiffel, better known for his tower in Paris, built several. Two German arch bridges of 1897 and 1898 were nearly as long in span as the Eads bridge; the Viaur Bridge in France (1898) exceeded it, with a central span of 721 feet. At Niagara Falls, an arch with an 840-foot span was completed in 1898. Known as the "Honeymoon Bridge," it was two-hinged in form, anchored by heavy steel pins to the rock walls of the gorge. During its first winter, a huge mass of floating ice battered at these pins but did not damage them. A concrete wall was built around the abutments to protect them, once the emergency had passed, and the bridge withstood later assaults until another ice jam in 1938 smashed it apart. Four years later, a second Niagara steel arch, the Rainbow Bridge, was in place. This slender arch, with a 950-foot span, was given fixed ends instead of hinges, so it would be better able to resist future ice floes. It is the longest fixed-ended steel arch bridge in the world.

The 1898 Honeymoon Bridge led to an even bigger steel arch in New York: the Hell Gate Bridge over the East River. It was begun in 1914. Three suspension bridges already crossed the East River, all of them far downtown—the Brooklyn, the Williamsburg, and the new Manhattan Bridge, carrying traffic between Manhattan and Brooklyn. In midtown there was the awkward cantilever Queensboro Bridge. The Hell Gate Bridge stood some miles to the north, where Long Island Sound met the East River. Its purpose was to serve as a railroad bridge carrying four tracks from Queens to Manhattan. Though the channel it spanned was narrow, the mingling tides of the East River and Long Island Sound created treacherous whirlpools. Its designer, Gustav Lindenthal, aimed to build a bridge so strong that neither the water conditions nor any conceivable train load could affect it.

He called for mammoth steel ribs, forming a double arch with heavy trusses linking the upper curve to the lower. Four sections of the lower curve, weighing 185 tons each, are still the biggest and heaviest single steel members ever used in bridge construction. Cranes weighing 315 tons were used to hoist these immense beams into place. Before the arch could be built, of course, its foundations had to be laid, and here Lindenthal was hard put to find rock strong enough to resist the thrust of his vast arch. Many caissons were sunk before a suitable location was uncovered. When a site was found, it turned out to have a grave flaw after all; once it had been excavated, a crevice in the underlying rock was discovered, 15 to 60 feet wide and of unknown depth. The fault in the rock had to be filled with concrete. The extremely taxing work was carried out under compressed air 70 feet below the river. One writer called it "a sort of gigantic dentistry job."

With the rock fault filled, Lindenthal began raising his mighty arch, building it out from its two towers toward the middle and anchoring it with temporary backstays. So carefully was the work done that when the halves of the arch met, 300 feet above the river,

The Hell Gate Bridge may well still be the strongest bridge ever built.

The Bayonne Bridge, the longest steel arch span in the world, joins Staten Island with the New Jersey mainland.

an adjustment of only five-sixteenths of an inch was needed to bring them into perfect alignment. The heavily stiffened deck of the Hell Gate Bridge was then suspended by steel ties to the two-hinged arch.

The 977-foot span of the Hell Gate Bridge made it the longest steel arch bridge of its day. It no longer holds that record, but it may well still be the strongest bridge ever built. Today the biggest locomotives in existence speed across it at sixty miles an hour without causing a stir in its 40,000,000 pounds of steel. The capacity of the bridge is reckoned at 76,000 pounds per lineal foot—52,000 pounds being the dead load of the bridge itself, the rest the moving live load. The burdens this railroad bridge carries are far beyond the limits of most other modern bridges.

Two huge steel arch bridges at opposite ends of the world soon replaced the Hell Gate Bridge as the longest of their type, though they do not have the older bridge's formidable carrying capacity. In Australia, a bridge across the harbor of the city of Sydney was opened in 1932, after great difficulties in construction. Its span was 1,650 feet. Almost simultaneously, a virtual twin steel arch bridge with a span a yard longer was built over the Kill van Kull, a body of water dividing Staten Island in New York from the New Jersey mainland. This bridge, which is still the longest steel arch span in the world, was the work of a Swiss-born engineer named Othmar H. Ammann, whom we will meet again in later chapters. It is known as the Bayonne Bridge.

Other steel arch bridges have followed. They are neither so heavy as the Hell Gate Bridge nor so long as the Bayonne Bridge, but they have their admirers all the same. Some have the roadway suspended below the arch, or running through the arch. New York City, which has such a multitude of great bridges, has an excellent example of an arch bridge whose roadway runs above the curve of the arch. This is the Henry Hudson Bridge over Spuyten Duyvil Creek between Manhattan and the Bronx.

New advances in bridge design and in the making of steel itself have made possible the construction of steel arch bridges of remarkable lightness and grace. The Birchenough Bridge in Rhodesia with a span of 1,080 feet and a slim suspended roadway, is one

The Henry Hudson Bridge, an arch bridge whose roadway runs above the curve of the arch, spans Spuyten Duyvil Creek between Manhattan and the Bronx.

such recent bridge of unusual elegance. Engineers today regard 2,500 feet as about the limit of a steel arch span, and it would not be surprising to see the Bayonne Bridge's span surpassed at some future site where a bridge of this type is deemed desirable.

Reinforced Concrete Bridges

The concrete bridge was another triumph of the venturesome engineers of the 19th century. Concrete is a man-made stone composed of sand, gravel, water, and Portland cement. Although the Romans had an excellent cement two thousand years ago, the Portland type of cement, which is used in making concrete, was not invented until 1824. Concrete itself poses the same problems as stone in bridge construction: its great weight makes any long span impossible to support. But reinforced concrete—concrete containing a skeleton of metal—is a different matter entirely.

A French gardener named Joseph Monier invented reinforced concrete in the 1860's. He was looking for a way to make big flowerpots from concrete. Monier discovered that when he inserted a network of iron wire in the wet concrete, his flowerpots were greatly strengthened, and did not have to be as bulky as pots of concrete alone. It did not take long for engineers to see the structural applications of Monier's method. Concrete was well suited to stand up under compression stresses, while the internal metal reinforcement resisted the tension stresses that concrete could not withstand.

Monier himself built one of the first reinforced concrete bridges in 1877, a span 50 feet long and 13 feet wide. The new material could be employed in beam and arch bridges, where compression was the main force exerted, but it was not suited for suspension spans, where the main force is one of tension. An Austrian engineer named Joseph Melan built a number of large reinforced concrete arch bridges, the biggest being the triple-arch Capellen Bridge in Minneapolis, with one span 400 feet long. French and Swiss bridge-builders developed a particular fondness for reinforced concrete, and built dozens of these bridges. At first, their bridges were nearly as massive as bridges of concrete alone would have been; but as

The Sandö Bridge in Sweden is one of the largest reinforced concrete spans ever built.

they gained confidence in their material, they began to build slender, breathtaking arches of dazzling lightness and beauty. An outstanding concrete arch of this sort was built in the United States over Russian Gulch, near Fort Bragg, California. It leaps soaringly from shore to shore, with vertical struts rising above it to support the roadway. Another fine example is the Waterloo Bridge in London, completed just before World War II. This is not an arch bridge, though it appears to be. Five long spans spring from 14-foot-thick piers, but four of them are simply beams of reinforced concrete with a purely decorative arch effect, while the fifth is supported by two cantilever arms. Not all spans that seem to curve are true arches, then. An arch must thrust its weight outward against its abutments, and this is not the case on the Waterloo Bridge, where the thrust is downward against the piers.

One of the longest reinforced concrete spans of all—exceeded only by a 1963 bridge in Sydney, Australia—is the Sandö Bridge in Sweden. Its 866-foot arch, rising to a center height of 130 feet, is only 8 feet thick at the crown, 14 feet at the ends. That means that the span is only about one one-hundredth as thick as it is long, a ratio that certainly would have bewildered a Roman architect. Pairs of circular columns support the roadway, which runs over the arch. Originally, the engineers planned to build the arch by erecting a temporary timber arch, floating it into position on barges, and using it as the base for the molds of the permanent bridge. However, this timber arch collapsed in 1939 during a period of damp weather, which weakened the wood. It was replaced by a wooden trestle propped up by thirteen groups of long piles reaching from the water, and the pouring of the concrete was completed by 1943.

In theory, arch bridges of reinforced concrete now can be constructed with spans of nearly a mile. However, no engineers have cared to make the experiment. The Sydney concrete arch, with its span of 910 feet, may never be surpassed. The variety of new bridge-building techniques that came into use at the beginning of the 20th century gives the designer many strings to his bow—but in the past 40 or 50 years, whenever a really big bridge must be built, the solution has almost always been the suspension bridge.

8:

Spanning
The Hudson

NO ONE HAS EVER CONSIDERED THE HUDSON RIVER, WHICH RUNS southward through New York State, a particularly demonic body of water. It is not a wild, turbulent stream like the Colorado. It never bursts its banks in a devastating rush, like the Mississippi. It has no crashing waterfalls. Slowly and placidly it flows to the sea, dropping gently about four feet in the 150 miles from Albany to New York City. The Hudson is a peaceful giant of a river.

A giant it is, however. As it nears the sea, its bed descends so that the salty water of the Atlantic enters the river, making the Hudson virtually an arm of the ocean. The breadth of New York Harbor, foundation of that city's greatness, is due to the invasion of the ocean on the Hudson's mouth. For many miles north of the harbor the river is thousands of feet wide, a lordly barrier of water cutting between New York and New Jersey.

While bridges multiplied at a breathless pace across the Mississippi, the Ohio, the Missouri, and the Tennessee, the Hudson went unbridged. Those other rivers, though far more rapid than the Hudson, had many sites less than 2,000 feet across; the lower Hudson rarely was much narrower than 4,000 feet. In the 19th century that was an impossible gap to span. The longest suspension bridge of the century, the Brooklyn Bridge, had a 1,600-foot span. No arch or cantilever bridge approached even that length. With the methods of the 19th century, the Hudson could be bridged only with a multiple-span bridge founded on many piers. That would interfere with the river's role as a major waterway, though. After the opening of the Erie Canal in 1825, linking Lake Erie to the Hudson, the river became an important channel for big shipping, and almost any multiple-span bridge would have blocked those ships. New Yorkers had no wish to choke their river with a bridge as Londoners had done in the 12th century.

Until 1888, ferries remained the only way to get from one Hudson shore to the other. The needs of the railroad industry finally produced a bridge at Poughkeepsie, many miles north of New York City. This was a high five-span cantilever bridge that would be no bar to shipping. Its use was almost entirely confined to trains, and ordinary citizens went on traveling by ferry.

The abrupt arrival of the automobile on the American scene early in the 20th century had as great an impact on bridge-building as the emergence of the railroad three generations before. By 1920, the automobile was no longer a rich man's plaything; $500 would buy anyone a "tin lizzie." The Sunday pleasure drive became a family custom. Like so many black beetles, the autos swarmed onto the roads and clustered at the ferry depots. The old ferries had not been designed for carrying bulky automobiles, and could only take a few at a time. The rest piled up on the shore to wait their turn. It might be only a 30-minute trip across the river, but it could take eight or ten hours to get aboard one of the hard-working ferryboats. Motorists demanded bridges across the Hudson, bridges that would permit a continuous flow of cars to cross.

The immediate result was the Bear Mountain Bridge, of the suspension type, with a 1,600-foot span and a roadway 150 feet above the navigation channel. That bridge, completed in 1924, linked the two sides of the river about midway between New York City and Poughkeepsie. In 1930, the Mid-Hudson Bridge at Poughkeepsie, another attractive suspension bridge, provided a second automobile crossing to the north. Its span was 1,500 feet. New York City, however, still had no Hudson bridge. The bustling metropolis now was adjoined by a thriving industrial and residential center on the western, or New Jersey, shore of the lower Hudson. Thousands of New Jerseyans had jobs in New York City, and vice versa. But there was no quick way to get across the river. Its width of well over 3,000 feet defied the bridge-builders. The sadly overcrowded Hudson ferries could not begin to deal with the growth in traffic.

Bridge construction, by this time, had become almost entirely a function of governments. Though the Brooklyn Bridge had been started by a private corporation, it had been taken over by a municipal body, and the same thing had befallen many other privately sponsored bridges of the 19th century. Only a city or state government had the financial resources to build and maintain a giant bridge.

The lower Hudson happened to be the boundary between New York and New Jersey, and that created some knotty political problems. The two states had not always been the best of neighbors. How could they cooperate in planning the Hudson crossings? Decades of bickering culminated in the signing of a treaty in 1921 that set up an agency known as the Port of New York Authority. This body, jointly controlled by both states, was given the task of developing the transportation links at the mouth of the Hudson.

Its first step was to construct the Holland Tunnel between lower Manhattan and New Jersey. The technique of tunnel construction had taken a great stride forward once an understanding of the causes of the bends was reached. Though tunnel workers, or "sandhogs," still occasionally suffered from caisson disease, the death tolls no longer were so shocking. A number of subway tunnels had been run between Manhattan and Brooklyn to supplement the three East River suspension bridges. The Holland Tunnel, though longer than those, did not present any unusual technical difficulties.

The tunnel, which was opened in 1927, was far downtown. The Port of New York Authority recognized the need for a Hudson crossing closer to the heart of Manhattan. The city had spread rapidly northward in the 20th century. Only a few years before, Times Square at 42nd Street had been considered an uptown location. Now, Times Square was midtown, and apartment houses were being erected all the way up to 225th Street at the northern end of the island. For a while there was talk of a midtown bridge in the 42nd

Street vicinity, but for various reasons a tunnel was decided on instead. By 1934, the first of the three Lincoln Tunnel tubes was under way.

The new uptown part of the city required a Hudson crossing, too. Otherwise, the millions of people in upper Manhattan and the Bronx would have to drive into congested lower Manhattan to get across the river, adding to a traffic problem that was already monumental. This uptown crossing, it was decided, would be a bridge. Wide as the Hudson was at that point, the Authority planned to fling across it an astounding suspension bridge with a span twice as great as that of any earlier bridge of any form.

A great bridge calls for a great bridge-builder. James Eads was long in his grave; Washington Roebling was in extreme old age. When the Port of New York Authority began planning its audacious Hudson River span in the mid-1920's, it chose a man who shared the vision and boldness of those earlier engineers: Othmar Hermann Ammann.

In personality, the Swiss-born Ammann was nothing like the energetic, ambitious Eads or the lively, fun-loving Washington Roebling. He was closer in character to old John Roebling—a man of few words, somewhat stiff and formal in his dealings with other people, fiercely and narrowly dedicated to the craft and science of engineering. Ammann was born in 1879 in the town of Schaffhausen, on the Rhine. He could trace his ancestry back to the 12th century. Ammanns had been famed as lawyers, clergymen, physicians, political leaders—but never before had a member of the family become an engineer.

When he was 25, Ammann came to the United States. He was just in time for the phenomenal burst of bridge-building activity that marked the opening of the 20th century. He became an assistant to Gustav Lindenthal, who was then the leading bridge engineer of the New York area. Lindenthal, in 1899, had proposed a suspension bridge across the Hudson which, if it had ever been built, would have been a true colossus. He planned a double deck 235 feet wide. The upper deck would carry 16 passenger-car lanes; the lower, a dozen subway-car tracks, two trolley tracks, two bus lanes, and a pair of 15-foot pedestrian walkways. The ponderous bridge never won support, but possibly Ammann had a chance to study its blueprints in Lindenthal's office, and caught from the older engineer the desire to span the Hudson from Manhattan.

When Ammann arrived, Lindenthal was involved in the Queensboro Bridge, of cantilever design. Before its completion, the Quebec Bridge suffered its first catastrophic collapse. Young Ammann was sent to Quebec in the fall of 1907 to study the cause of the disaster, for the Quebec Bridge had been a cantilever, and Lindenthal did not wish to have his bridge share its fate. Ammann returned with the opinion that the cantilever type of construction held hidden pitfalls, and that engineers did not yet fully understand the stresses involved in building such bridges. Lindenthal examined his nearly completed Queensboro Bridge and decided that it would be safest to cut its train tracks from four to two. That involved spending $4,000,000 extra to build a subway tunnel a block from the bridge, but it prevented a repetition of the Quebec calamity.

Lindenthal's next project was the massive Hell Gate Bridge, and Ammann assisted in the construction of this enormous steel arch. Hardly had the work begun, in 1914, than World War I broke out. Ammann was called back to Switzerland for military service. Gustav Lindenthal found a new assistant, a native New Yorker named David Steinman, who served with him on the Hell Gate work and on many later bridges. Steinman became one of America's leading bridge engineers, and his reputation made him Ammann's great rival in future years.

When the war ended, Ammann returned to the United States and became the chief engineer for the newly founded Port of New York Authority. His first important job for the Authority was the Bayonne Bridge, the giant steel arch over the Kill van Kull. Once that enterprise was under way, he turned his attention to the bridge across the Hudson.

The George Washington Bridge

Ammann's main experience had been with arch bridges. No arch could ever span this gulf, though. The site for the bridge had been chosen: it would rise from Fort Washington on the New York

The George Washington Bridge under construction.

side at 178th Street in Manhattan, crossing to that wall of basalt
cliffs in New Jersey known as the Palisades. In 1925 Ammann made
his first test borings for the foundations of the future George
Washington Bridge.

In Detroit, a suspension bridge with a span of 1,850 feet was
already under construction. Upon its completion in 1929, this bridge
held the record for length of span—but only for two years. Ammann's bridge nearly doubled that span, at 3,500 feet. Such a
bridge would need titanic towers, and Ammann provided them:
steel pylons 595 feet high, as tall as a 60-story skyscraper.

So far as methods of construction went, the George Washington Bridge followed the pattern set by the Roeblings 60 years earlier for their Brooklyn Bridge, on a much larger scale. In September, 1927, construction started on the foundations of the piers. Instead of using pneumatic caissons, with all the risks that working under compressed air entailed, Ammann chose to build cofferdams and excavate for his foundations in the dry. The cofferdams were the biggest ever used for a bridge. Made of steel sheet piling, they had double walls eight feet apart, and were driven to depths ranging from 40 feet, inshore on the Jersey side, to 85 feet on the river face. The space between the double walls was filled with concrete. Steel and timber struts braced the interior of the cofferdams against the pressure of the water.

Pumping the cofferdams dry was a slow job, even with the most efficient modern equipment, for they measured 108 feet by 99 feet at the base. When they were dry, the bedrock was prepared to receive the weight of the piers, and then the two great towers were erected.

Spinning the four cables followed. First two temporary footbridges were strung across the span, a yard below the position that the main cables would occupy. Workmen scrambling along these footbridges guided the traveling wheels as they made their thousands of round trips, carrying the wires that would compose the cables. Each wire, a fifth of an inch in diameter, had a strength of 98 tons per square inch. The bridge required 105,000 miles of this wire in all, enough to go four times around the Earth. Each of the four cables was 36 inches in diameter and contained 26,474 wires. Special squeezing machines traveled along the cables, gripping the wires together every two to four feet and forcing them into a compact circular form.

When the cables were in place, vertical steel hangers were suspended from them to carry the roadway. The four cables were securely anchored. On the New Jersey side, they ran into tunnels cut deep into the rock of the Palisades. No such cliff existed on the New York side, so the engineers created one, fashioning a block of concrete of gigantic size to receive the pull of the cables.

The steelwork of the roadway was built outward from the towers. As each section of the deck was fastened in place, derricks

The George Washington Bridge, viewed from Palisades Interstate Park.

moved out onto it and hoisted the next section to its position. The largest of these derricks weighed 62 tons. The roadway, 119 feet wide, naturally exerted a tremendous pull on the cables as it grew. When the entire deck was in place and the cables had reached their full stretch, one task remained. A wrapping machine moved slowly along the cables, binding them tightly in a sheath of wire.

Ammann's original design for the George Washington Bridge called for it to carry two decks, linked by a 29-foot-high truss. The upper deck would carry automobiles, the lower deck an interstate rapid-transit line. When work began on the bridge in 1927, the United States was enjoying an era of booming prosperity and such optimistic plans were not considered rash. But in the fall of 1929 the stock market collapsed, ushering in the time of economic hardships known as the Great Depression. Many dreams of the boom days had to be abandoned. The rapid-transit line was one; the second deck of the George Washington Bridge was another. Eight lanes of automobile traffic would be sufficient for now, the Port of New York Authority reckoned; the lower deck could always be added twenty or thirty years later, if traffic conditions required it.

When the second deck was cancelled, Ammann took the surprising step of eliminating the big stiffening truss as well. This was not primarily an economy move, for no bridge-builder ever tries to pinch pennies at the expense of safety. Although every suspension bridge in the last century had guarded its deck with a stiffening truss, Ammann calculated that his bridge could get along without one. His roadway was so heavy that it could withstand wind forces of almost any intensity, and a truss would add little or nothing to the strength of the basic design. So the finished bridge was unique in its beauty: a flat ribbon of steel strung between two mighty towers.

In 1962, the trusses were at last added—not because the bridge had shown a tendency to be unstable, but simply because the time had come to install the lower deck. Othmar Ammann, eighty-three years old and still an active engineer, supervised the building of the second deck and the heavy truss. The beauty of the original bridge was marred, some people felt, but the relentless growth of interstate traffic had made the new lanes necessary.

Another last-minute decision during the construction of the bridge stemmed both from motives of economy and a desire for architectural loveliness. The design called for the towers to be encased in masonry, as had been done on the Brooklyn Bridge and on many other suspension bridges. But the bare metal struts of the towers had a stark handsomeness of their own, and as the bridge neared completion in 1931 a number of art critics suggested that they be left exposed. Since the limestone facing was not necessary to the strength of the bridge, and since the ever-deepening Depression was making cost-cutting necessary, the towers were left uncovered, greatly enhancing the attractiveness of the bridge.

The George Washington Bridge was opened in October, 1931. No particular drama had accompanied its construction. Men had risked their lives high above the river to build the bridge, yes, but there had been little of the sense of epic struggle that marked the work on the St. Louis Bridge or the Brooklyn Bridge. Quietly, soberly, Othmar Ammann and his co-workers had created the world's biggest bridge. With that single majestic span thrown across the lordly Hudson, Ammann had shown that the suspension bridge was indeed the ideal form for great lengths. His George Washington Bridge was virtually a textbook demonstration of the right way to carry out such a job. It was so strong a bridge that it was even able to endure the crash landing of a small airplane on the central traffic lanes the day after Christmas, 1965.

The Hudson has been bridged many times since the completion of the George Washington. But the other spans, all of them upstream from New York City, did not require the sort of spectacular engineering demanded by the Manhattan-to-New Jersey site. First came the Rip Van Winkle Bridge at Catskill, New York, completed in 1935. This bridge consists of a series of trusses, with a cantilever span rising over the navigation channel in the middle of the river. Twenty years later, the New York State Thruway Bridge was added at Nyack, about 30 miles north of the George Washington Bridge. Better known as the Tappan Zee Bridge, this one actually crosses the Hudson at one of its widest points. The water is fairly shallow there, though, and much of the bridge's overall length of 16,000 feet is made up of a series of 50-foot beam spans and of 20 steel trusses 235 to 250 feet long. The central unit of the big bridge is of cantilever type, with a main span of 1,212 feet flanked by a pair of 602-foot anchoring arms. A novel feature of the Tappan Zee Bridge was the use of eight concrete piers of buoyant design as the foundations of the main section. These huge boxes play a pontoon-like role, their buoyancy offsetting the downward thrust of the bridge's weight, and reducing the dead load on the foundations by 80 per cent.

The Tappan Zee Bridge is by no means the longest bridge in the world. That honor must go to the Tsao-chow Bridge across the Yellow River in China. It runs for some ninety miles, and consists mostly of beam spans supported by piles in shallow water, with suspension, truss, or cantilever spans in the deeper places. In the United States, the record is held by the 24-mile long low-level structure over Lake Ponchartrain, Louisiana, completed in 1956. That bridge has 2,235 concrete spans 56 feet long, and eleven larger spans. When engineers speak of a "big" bridge, they do not refer

The Bronx-Whitestone Bridge, spanning the East River, is one of the six great bridges that Othmar Ammann built for New York.

Throgs Neck Bridge under construction. General view of top of the Bronx anchorage. Distribution slab is complete except for cantilever section.

View looking northwest of the massive Throgs Neck Bridge tower caisson.

to overall length but to the length of the main span—the distance between one pier and another.

The next Hudson River bridge was the Kingston-Rhinecliff Bridge, completed early in 1957. This was the work of David Steinman, Ammann's long-time rival for the big bridge jobs. A mile and a half long from abutment to abutment, it was made up of ten truss spans 300 to 800 feet long, with the largest units centered over the two navigable channels of the river. Two more Hudson River bridges have been completed since then, and perhaps others will be called for as the growth of upper New York State makes them necessary.

Othmar Ammann had no hand in the Hudson bridges after the George Washington, but that does not mean he was idle in the years that followed its completion. As we have seen, he remained an active bridge-builder until extreme old age, and was in charge of the double-decking of the George Washington Bridge, finished in 1962 at a cost of $145,000,000—nearly twice what the entire original bridge had cost. And a later chapter will tell how he put the capstone on his brilliant career in 1964 with the Verrazano-Narrows Bridge, a suspension span even greater than the George Washington.

In the 33 years between his two magnificent suspension bridges, Ammann was a busy engineer indeed. He linked the three New York City Boroughs of Queens, Manhattan, and the Bronx with the elaborate Triborough Bridge, which is actually a series of bridges over three miles long, including a suspension bridge, five truss spans, a section that lifts vertically to let ships pass, and thousands of feet of approach road. He also built two large suspension bridges which would be considered important tourist attractions if they were located anywhere but in New York City, where they play minor roles compared with the George Washington and the Verrazano-Narrows Bridges. These are the 1939 Bronx-Whitestone Bridge, with a span of 2,300 feet, and the Throgs Neck Bridge, finished in 1961, with an 1,800-foot span. In all, Othmar Ammann gave New York six great bridges—the Bayonne, the George Washington, the Triborough, the Bronx-Whitestone, the Throgs Neck, and the Verrazano-Narrows—and served as an assis-

The completed Throgs Neck Bridge, looking north from Clearview Park.

The Walt Whitman Bridge links Philadelphia with Camden, New Jersey.

tant engineer during the construction of a seventh, the Hell Gate Bridge. Late in his life, Ammann lived in an apartment on the 32nd floor of a New York hotel, and from his windows he could see all seven of these engineering triumphs.

Most of his important accomplishments were carried out in and about New York, but he sometimes accepted assignments from other cities. Thus he built the Walt Whitman Bridge in Philadelphia, to name just one. And, a few years after the George Washington Bridge was a reality, when the city of San Francisco prepared to top that span with an even mightier suspension bridge, one of the engineers called on for advice was the man who knew more about big suspension bridges than anyone else in the world—Othmar H. Ammann.

9:

A Bridge For
The Golden Gate

FEW CITIES CAN CLAIM LOVELIER PHYSICAL SURROUNDINGS THAN SAN Francisco, California. It rises on steep hills at the tip of a long peninsula, framed on the western side by the blue Pacific, on the east by San Francisco Bay. On a day of bright sunshine, San Francisco glitters like a jewel. At other times, heavy fog rolls in from the water, giving the city a haunted, romantic beauty.

San Francisco Bay, a nearly landlocked body of water fifty miles in length, provides a splendid harbor for this handsome city. But the big bay long left San Francisco isolated on its peninsula. The city is actually quite small in area, covering just 44.6 square miles, in contrast to the 315 square miles of New York and the 454.8 square miles of Los Angeles. Inevitably, its population overflowed onto the other shores of San Francisco Bay, and the neighboring cities of Berkeley and Oakland were founded. Many people came to work each day in San Francisco and returned to one of the outlying cities at night. Like Manhattan, San Francisco became the hub of a populous region, and bridges became necessary to connect the various sections of the Bay area.

You can get a good idea of the layout of the Bay area by crooking the index finger and thumb of your right hand so that their tips nearly meet. The oval space within your bent fingers is San Francisco Bay. The tip of your thumb is San Francisco. Facing it, on the tip of your index finger, is suburban Marin County. Oakland and Berkeley are side by side on the inner curve of your hand, across the bay from San Francisco. The narrow opening between San Francisco and Marin County is the strait that connects the bay with the waters of the Pacific Ocean. This is the strait known as the Golden Gate.

San Franciscans long dreamed of bridges that would span the Golden Gate, on one hand, and that would cross the bay to link their city with Oakland, on the other. As early as the 1860's, when San Francisco was only a small pioneer town, such bridges were suggested, and just as quickly rejected as impossible. The two projects both were difficult, but for different reasons. San Francisco Bay is eight miles across at the San Francisco-Oakland point, so any kind of bridge crossing would have to have a great many spans, whose foundations would rest in water 200 to 300 feet deep. Such depths were more than twice as great as any that could be handled in the 19th century. As for the Golden Gate, its narrowest point was about a mile in width, which led some optimists to think it could be spanned by a huge suspension bridge. But the water is hundreds of feet deep. To add to the problems of pier construction, the Pacific tides sweep in and out of the strait four times a day, moving with a fierce rush that would make construction work hazardous if not entirely inconceivable.

A further point to consider was San Francisco's vulnerability to earthquakes. The city lies along an enormous crevice in the earth known as the San Andreas Fault, and from time to time the sides of this crevice shift, causing the crust of the earth to shudder for hundreds of miles. In 1906, the San Andreas Fault heaved and bucked and brought San Francisco tumbling into ruins. New York City, which has never had a real earthquake, could spend millions of dollars on bridges and expect them to stand forever. San Francisco would be taking a gamble if it engaged in any such large-scale construction.

Somehow, the earthquake and the ensuing terrible fire of 1906 served to spur the enthusiasm of the San Franciscans for their city. The rubble was cleared, the downtown section was rebuilt on a scale greater than ever, and—as though out to show the world that their spirits were undaunted—the people of San Francisco began to plan their "impossible" bridges. Neither the pessimism of the experts nor the threat of future earthquakes seemed to matter.

An engineer named Joseph B. Strauss began serious studies of the Golden Gate project. In 1919, he drew up a plan for a giant suspension bridge across the strait. About the same time, C. H. Purcell made his first sketches for what was to become the San Francisco-Oakland Bay Bridge.

Early progress on both bridges was slow. The California Legislature's approval was needed, and the lawmakers insisted on careful examination of the proposals before they agreed to permit construction. The United States Government had to be consulted also. San Francisco Bay was the most important harbor on the West Coast, and the authorities in Washington were concerned with what might happen to that harbor if a Golden Gate Bridge were to collapse and block the waterway to shipping. Calculations were produced showing that even if the bridge fell, the water was so deep that big ships could still enter the harbor over the wreckage, and in 1924 the Department of War, which had jurisdiction over the case, gave its assent.

Even then, work could not begin. Many people in and about San Francisco did not want the big bridges to be built, and they went to court to prevent construction. Some of these people were taxpayers who resented the immense cost of the bridges; they preferred to go on riding ferries. The operators of the ferry lines also objected, for they would be put out of business by the bridges. Not until 1930 were the last legal hurdles swept aside. By 1933, the plans for the bridges were complete, and construction commenced on both of them that year.

The Bay Bridge was the bigger project, the Golden Gate Bridge the more difficult one. San Franciscans were treated to the unique experience of watching two of the greatest engineering feats of all time proceeding simultaneously.

San Francisco-Oakland Bay Bridge

C. H. Purcell, the chief engineer of the Bay Bridge, had an eight-mile gap to span. Four and a half miles would be over water;

the rest of the distance included approach spans and the crossing of an island in the middle of the bay. This island, known as Yerba Buena, actually made two separate projects out of the Bay Bridge.

More than a mile of water stood between Yerba Buena and the San Francisco shore. For this western section of the crossing, Purcell had a choice of near-impossibilities. He could try to build a single suspension span more than a mile long, or he could attempt to sink intermediate piers in water that was over 200 feet deep. He decided on the latter course. He would build a central anchorage and use it as the midway support for *two* end-to-end suspension bridges, each with a span of 2,310 feet. As a result, San Francisco Bay has the only double suspension bridge in the world.

The central anchorage had to be founded on bedrock, and bedrock was 225 feet under the surface. Men could not work in an ordinary pneumatic caisson at such a depth, so special techniques had to be devised. The world's largest caisson was built, measuring 92 by 197 feet and weighing 6,000 tons when it left the shipyard. It consisted of 55 vertical steel cylinders, each one 15 feet in diameter, open at the bottom but equipped with a water-tight, removable cover at the top.

The monstrous caisson was towed to position, anchored, and lowered through the water, its descent controlled by the compressed air within the sealed steel cylinders. When the caisson hovered just a few feet above the mud of the bay floor, its weight was abruptly increased by an adjustment in the air pressure. It dropped swiftly, its cutting edge slicing into the mud. Next, the spaces between the interior steel cylinders were filled with concrete to give the caisson solidity. Then the tops of the cylinders were taken off, and buckets were lowered into the cylinders to scoop out the muck of the bottom. Gradually the mud underlying the caisson was dredged out. The caisson settled lower and lower. Sometimes it tilted ominously to its side, and divers in suits went down to supervise the leveling job, phoning up orders to increase or lower the air pressure in certain cylinders.

At last all the mud had been scooped from beneath the caisson and it rested on bedrock. But the rock sloped, and the foundation had to be flat. Dynamite could not be used within the caisson; a

Overhead shot of the San Francisco-Oakland Bay Bridge.

five-ton steel weight was dropped through each cylinder to break up the rock, and divers cleared the fragments away. When the caisson was horizontal on the rock floor, the cylinders were filled with concrete and construction of the pier began. It took 160,000 cubic yards of concrete to build the pier, which rises 300 feet above the high-water level.

The same technique was used for two tower foundations for the suspension bridges, one between San Francisco and the central anchorage, the other between the central anchorage and Yerba Buena. Two other tower foundations were built in shallower water, and the end anchorages were put in place at either shore, making seven big piers in all. Construction of the twin suspension bridges followed in the usual way. Temporary footbridges were used during the spinning of the cables, which were 28¾ inches in diameter and contained 17,464 wires apiece. Steel hangers were strung from these cables, and the roadways were attached, in units weighing up to 204 tons that were put in place by cranes. The central anchorage was the point where the cables met; they rose from there to the two deep-water towers of the two suspension bridges, sloped again, rose to the shallow-water pair of towers, and sloped once more to their shoreside piers. Besides the two 2,310-foot main spans, there were four side spans of 1,160 feet each in this complex of suspension bridges.

Yerba Buena Island itself, rocky and high, was crossed by a roadway 3,585 feet long. Of this, 540 feet passed through a tunnel 76 feet wide and 58 feet high. To dig this tunnel, more than 75,000 cubic yards of rock and earth had to be excavated.

The eastern leg of the crossing, between Yerba Buena and the Oakland shore, received an entirely different sort of bridge— a cantilever whose 1,400-foot span made it the longest bridge of this type in the United States, and the fourth longest in the world. (It has since been surpassed by a bridge in Louisiana.) Two side spans of 512 feet each flank this central unit. The roadway it carries rises 185 feet above the high-water level, to insure a clear passage for big shipping below. Three other large spans and fourteen short ones complete this eastern section of the lengthy Bay Bridge.

Nighttime view of the San Francisco-Oakland Bay Bridge.

The entire bridge, with its multitude of spans, was finished and opened to traffic in November, 1936. For sheer complexity and massiveness, it has rarely been equalled, and the unusual technique by which the deep-water anchorages of the western suspension bridges were laid made it an engineering landmark. Like many great bridges, this one exacted a high price in human life. Two dozen workmen were killed in accidents during its construction, and more than a thousand suffered serious injuries.

Golden Gate Bridge

The San Francisco-Oakland Bay Bridge was such a gigantic enterprise, and was made up of so many components, that its construction baffled rather than thrilled the onlookers. By contrast, the drama of the Golden Gate Bridge was much more immediate. This was a single bridge of stunning beauty, erected at a site perhaps more taxing than any other ever spanned, and the struggle of man against the sea reached an almost unbearable level of suspense.

Joseph Strauss, the engineer whose name is most closely associated with the Golden Gate Bridge, made and discarded several designs, over a period of eleven years, before he settled on his final plan in 1930. He settled upon a suspension type whose 4,200-foot span would exceed by 700 feet the George Washington Bridge then nearing completion in the east. There would be two side spans leading from the towers to the shore, each 1,125 feet in length, giving the bridge an overall span length of 6,450 feet— almost 1,700 feet longer than the total length of Othmar Ammann's bridge across the Hudson.

Fibers of steel and rock-steady piers would enable Strauss to erect this titan. He did not anticipate any serious problems with the superstructure of the bridge, for Ammann had already shown that a suspension span nearly as large could be constructed, and Strauss had called Ammann in as a consultant to advise him on the Golden Gate project. The test of Strauss' engineering skill lay in the building of the foundations, notably the foundation of the south pier.

That pier was to be built 1,125 feet from the shore, virtually

The Golden Gate Bridge under construction, June 16, 1935.

in the open sea. Ocean tides, fogs, and storms all would buffet the construction workers. The exposed position of the site would make it impossible to use floating equipment during the work; the wild sea would sweep away the barges customarily employed to carry construction materials for a big bridge.

Strauss decided to build an access trestle—a temporary wooden bridge—over which materials could be carried to the site of the south pier. This was no small feat in itself. The piles of the trestle had to be fixed in the bedrock of the ocean floor, which entailed blasting holes in the rock far below the waves. The 1,100-foot trestle was completed late in 1932. A few months later, a freighter lost in a fog rammed into it and ripped away the middle 300 feet. The damage was repaired, and almost at once a savage storm smashed the trestle apart, demolishing an 800-foot stretch. Once more the trestle was rebuilt, and in the fall of 1933 excavation was finished at the site of the pier.

Actually two piers were built, one within the other. To protect his tower against the force of the sea and against fogbound ships, Strauss chose to construct an outer ring, or "fender," of concrete. Before the fender could be built, it was necessary to blast the bedrock to a horizontal level. Some 60,000 cubic yards of rock had to be removed, at a depth 100 feet below the surface.

The blasting was accomplished in an unusual way. Steel pipes lowered from boats drilled holes two feet wide and two feet deep in the rock of the ocean floor. Small bombs were inserted in these holes, and by repeated blasting the holes were enlarged to a depth of about 18 feet. Now large bombs, 20 feet long, 8 inches wide, containing 200 pounds of dynamite each, were rammed into the holes and detonated six at a time. Huge masses of rock were blasted loose this way and dredged away by an extraordinary floating derrick. The derrick's big scoop bucket picked up big boulders and swung them out into the sea, where the tide swiftly swept them away from the area of construction.

In March, 1934, pouring of concrete for the fender began. It was composed of 22 sections, each 33 feet long, arranged in a broad oval. The first unit was built at the end of the access trestle. Concrete was poured into a steel framework below the water, and the section was built up until it reached fifteen feet above the surface. Other sections were added on both sides, and so on until a concrete ring 155 feet wide and 299 feet long took shape, enclosing a basin of water nearly 100 feet deep.

A large opening was left in the eastern wall of the fender. The top sections at this end rose no higher than 40 feet below the surface level. On October 8, 1934, the giant pneumatic caisson that was to serve as the foundation for the pier was towed through the opening in the fender. The caisson weighed 8,000 tons and measured 90 by 180 feet.

It was thought that the task of lowering the caisson to bedrock would be relatively easy, sheltered as it was by the concrete wall of the fender. But things did not work out that way. The morning after the caisson entered the fender, a storm arose that sent violent Pacific swells surging into the opening of the fender's eastern wall. Big as it was, the caisson was tossed about like a cork. Several of its mooring ropes snapped, and it threatened to smash the fender itself apart.

There was no time to close the gap in the fender by pouring the concrete for the final sections. Confronted with the need to make an instant decision of heartbreaking scope, the engineers decided to sacrifice the caisson to save the fender. It was towed out to sea, and a new construction plan was devised overnight. The caisson, moored now to tugboats, broke free and swept wildly through the sea. It had to be destroyed with dynamite, 30 miles off shore, to keep it from becoming a menace to shipping.

Instead of using a caisson, the bridge-builders now resolved to turn their fender into a cofferdam. They completed the bathtub-shaped ring of the fender, raised its walls to a height of 15 feet above the sea on all sides, and poured new concrete within it to strengthen it. Then they pumped it dry and proceeded to build their pier. Pouring in concrete at a rate of a hundred cubic yards an hour, they brought the pier to a height of 44 feet above low water level by the last day of 1934. After the top of the concrete pier had been ground dead level, the steel slabs that would serve as the base members of the suspension towers were put in place. There were 38 of these slabs, each weighing five tons.

By February 1, 1935, construction could begin on the tower above the south pier. The north pier had long since been finished, and its tower was already in place. Building that pier had seemed almost easy, compared with the grim and grueling work on the south pier. The north pier was founded on rock in 20 feet of water, at the base of a cliff. A cofferdam of steel and timber was put down, and the pier base, 80 by 160 feet and weighing 50,000 tons, was assembled within it.

The suspension towers were novel in design. They each consisted of two columns joined by X-shaped braces. Each column was built up out of steel cells 3 feet 6 inches square with walls seven-eighths of an inch thick. At the base the columns were 97 cells across, but the towers tapered so that there were only 21 cells

The completed Golden Gate Bridge, one of the world's tallest and longest single-span suspension bridges.

across the top. Some of the sections of these towers weighed 85 tons. Together, the towers required 45,000 tons of steel, or more than was used for the entire structure of the cantilever bridge of Quebec.

When the 746-foot-high towers were complete, late in 1935, the spinning of the cables could begin. The contract for these cables was awarded to the company that had spun the cables for the

George Washington Bridge. The lessons learned in building that bridge proved useful. For the first time, the strands making up the cables varied in size according to their positions along the bridge. The wire used was the standard fifth-of-an-inch thickness, but some strands contained as few as 256 wires, others as many as 472. Eight sets of traveling wheels were used, driven by electric motors. The new methods permitted 271 tons of cable to be spun a day, as against only 61 tons a day on the George Washington Bridge. The spinning of the vast web began on November 11, 1935, and was finished the following May.

Now the deck went into place—a roadway 90 feet wide, 265 feet above the water. Cranes mounted on the towers hoisted the first units of the steelwork into position. When these had been fastened to the hangers, the cranes moved out onto them to erect the next units, and so on until they met in the middle of the span. By the beginning of 1937, all the steelwork was in place and the paving of the roadway began.

During the arduous years of construction, there had been many accidents on the bridge, but no fatalities. The old adage that every bridge must claim a life was not to be denied, though. Safety nets strung below the decks had saved a number of men who had lost their balance while working. But in February, 1937, while a dozen men were at work on a scaffold, an aluminum link holding the scaffold snapped. Men and scaffold plunged into the safety net, which was not strong enough to take the sudden burden. The workers dropped to the water. Three were rescued, but the rest were swept away by the current.

A few months later, in May, 1937, the Golden Gate Bridge was formally placed in service, six months after the dedication of the Bay Bridge. It had cost $35,000,000; the much larger Bay Bridge had cost $61,000,000. The George Washington Bridge had held the record for longest span only five and a half years. The Golden Gate Bridge was destined to wear those laurels until 1964, when it was exceeded at last by New York's Verrazano-Narrows Bridge.

The impossible had been achieved. Bridges now spanned the

Golden Gate and San Francisco Bay—bridges of phenomenal size, bridges strong enough to withstand an earthquake even more severe than the one of 1906. By refusing to admit the impossibility of founding a pier in the Pacific Ocean or in 225 feet of bay water, the San Franciscans had spun glittering bands of steel to bind their region together.

10:

The Death of Galloping Gertie

THE VISION OF OLD JOHN ROEBLING HAD BEEN TRANSLATED INTO
concrete and steel. "Any span inside of 3,000 feet is practicable,"
he had written in 1867. "A span of 1,600 feet or more can be made
just as safe, and as strong in proportion, as a span of 100 feet.
The larger span is not a question of practicability, but simply a
question of cost."

Brooklyn Bridge was still unbuilt when Roebling wrote those
words, and a suspension bridge with a span even as great as 1,600
feet seemed like an unreal fantasy to many of his contemporaries.
He and his son had built that bridge. Other engineers had constructed bridges one or two hundred feet longer. Suddenly, in the
1930's, bridge-builders were jumping to a new order of accomplishment. Othmar Ammann's George Washington Bridge and Joseph
Strauss' Golden Gate Bridge inspired a sense of confidence that
verged almost on giddiness. With the steel cable at his command,
an engineer could hope to put a suspension span across ever more
awesome gulfs.

Not only were suspension bridges getting longer, they were
growing more graceful. The Roeblings had stiffened their Brooklyn
Bridge with a sturdy array of trusses and stays, and for fifty years
that had set the style. Ammann had dispensed with trusses entirely,

since the roadway of the George Washington Bridge was so heavy and wide. The Golden Gate Bridge needed trusses because of the strong winds that blew through the strait, but these trusses were only 25 feet high, in contrast to the 40-foot truss on the much shorter span of New York's Williamsburg Bridge. Calculations showed that in a gale blowing at 120 miles an hour, the mid-span point of the Golden Gate's deck would sway 21 feet to either side. But this was not considered dangerous. Suspension bridges were supposed to have a certain degree of flexibility.

The bridges that came immediately after the Golden Gate Bridge carried the trend toward lightness even further. Othmar Ammann's Bronx-Whitestone Bridge, completed in 1939, had no stiffening truss. Its roadway was lined by plate girders 11 feet high. Since the girders, being solid, would take the brunt of a high wind with greater impact than open trusswork, Ammann was showing unusual confidence in his calculations by using such a brace. Yet his figures showed that the Bronx-Whitestone was a safe bridge, strong enough to withstand any combination of wind forces and load stresses.

That bridge had a span of 2,300 feet, and its deck was 74 feet wide. By the standards of the past, it was narrow in proportion to its length, but not unusually so. The ratio of deck width to length of span was 1:31, about the same as the ratios of the George Washington and the Bay Bridge suspensions. The Golden Gate had a much higher ratio, 1:47—that is, its deck was narrower in proportion to the length of its span than the other bridges.

Tacoma-Narrows Bridge

In 1940 a bridge was opened whose statistics made some engineers rub their eyes in disbelief. This was the Tacoma-Narrows Bridge in the state of Washington, crossing Puget Sound to link the Olympic Peninsula with the rest of the state. It was the third longest suspension bridge in the world, with a span of 2,800 feet. But its roadway was only 39 feet wide. The deck-to-span ratio was an amazing 1:72, the highest of any suspension bridge ever constructed.

On the Golden Gate Bridge, with its high ratio of 1:47, the

designers had provided stability with the 25-foot-high stiffening truss. Incredibly, the Tacoma-Narrows Bridge was braced merely by an 8-foot-high plate girder. Not only was it narrower in proportion to its length than any other suspension span, it had the least amount of stiffening, except for the wide and sturdy George Washington Bridge!

The designer of such a bridge had to be either very foolhardy or very sure of his skill. Leon S. Moisseiff of New York, the designing engineer, was not considered a foolhardy man. At the age of sixty-eight, he was one of the most respected bridge experts in the country, ranking with Othmar Ammann and David Steinman. Moisseiff's career went back to 1897, and he had taken part in the planning of virtually every big American bridge of modern times. He had helped to design the Manhattan Bridge, the Hell Gate arch, the George Washington and the Triborough Bridges, the Ambassador Bridge in Detroit, The Golden Gate, the Bay Bridge, and the Bronx-Whitestone. Moisseiff had been a major contributor to the evolution of longer, slimmer suspension bridges. He had been closely connected with the trend toward a higher width-to-length ratio and smaller stiffening trusses. He had led the way toward the replacement of the truss with the much more attractive plate girder, a solid, shallow metal strip lining the roadway. Experiments in wind tunnels with model bridges had shown him that bridges in the new style would be safe in the face of mighty gales and heavy loads. If he was willing to stake his reputation on the startling design of the Tacoma-Narrows Bridge, it was safe to assume that he had explored every possibility.

The design was accepted. Millions of dollars of bonds were sold to finance construction. On July 1, 1940, Leon Moisseiff's Tacoma-Narrows Bridge was opened to traffic.

In an era of beautiful new bridges, this one was something special. Since it was not expected to have a big traffic load, it had only two lanes for automobiles, and pedestrian sidewalks. Long and narrow, its clean lines uncluttered by any spidery trusses, it vaulted in a dazzling sweep from shore to shore, a structure of great delicacy and elegance.

Even before it opened, the Tacoma-Narrows Bridge was stirring some concern among local authorities. When a high wind hit the bridge broadside, the deck would sway from side to side. This in itself was not alarming; every suspension bridge swings a few feet under wind action. But the deck of the Tacoma-Narrows Bridge also had an odd tendency to go up and down. Rippling waves appeared in the roadway, and it fluttered like a carpet in the breeze. These vertical movements had also been observed in the decks of other suspension bridges, but never to such a great extent.

Leon Moisseiff's computations and wind-tunnel experiments showed that the bridge should be able to resist gales up to 120 miles an hour in force. That was fine; but why did the bridge jump around so in winds of only thirty to forty miles an hour? Diagonal ties were installed at mid-span to cut down on movements between the deck and the cables.

The up-and-down rippling of the deck continued. It could not fail to be noticed by the public. A driver crossing the bridge when a breeze was blowing would see the car in front of him seem to sink into the roadway, as though a hump had suddenly risen in the deck. Sometimes the movement would be so great that the bending of the bridge would cause the car in front to disappear from view altogether for a moment. Washington newspapers devoted much space to analysis of the theory behind the bridge, citing designer Moisseiff's high reputation. The people of the state were told that their bridge was the last word in modern bridge design, and that there was absolutely no cause for alarm.

The flexible bridge fascinated the public. It got the fond nickname, "Galloping Gertie." On days when a strong wind was blowing, it became a popular amusement to drive out to the bridge and watch Galloping Gertie leap about.

Galloping Gertie staged her most spectacular performance on the morning of November 7, 1940, four months after her dedication. At dawn, a moderate wind began to blow, and by 7 A.M. it had reached a force of 42 miles per hour—no gale, just a good stiff breeze. Galloping Gertie responded in her now-familiar way. The east span remained still, the long central span was rippling slightly, and the west span was rippling more than slightly. Clark Eldridge, a bridge engineer employed by the Washington Toll Bridge Authority, drove across the bridge at 8:30 on his way to work. He observed the behavior of Galloping Gertie, but, as he reported later, "All of these motions . . . were considerably less than had occurred many times before so I came to the office at about nine o'clock."

By the time Eldridge reached his office, the deck of the bridge was whipping up and down in waves thirty feet high, and occasionally twisting at an angle of nearly 45 degrees as it rose and fell. The keepers of the tollbooths decided to close the bridge to traffic. An excited crowd gathered to watch the gyrations of the tortured span. Movie cameras were set up to record the action. A newspaperman was driving across the bridge when further traffic was halted. The other cars on the bridge made it to safety, but he did not think that he could get his car across. Parking the vehicle a third of the way out on the bridge, he climbed from it and scurried on foot along the heaving roadway to solid ground. The marooned car slid back and forth as the deck continued to writhe.

At ten o'clock, word reached the office of the Washington Toll Bridge Authority that Galloping Gertie was about to break apart. Engineer Eldridge hurried to the scene. "The center span was swaying wildly, it being possible first to see the entire bottom side as it swung into a semi-vertical position and then the entire roadway," he told a board of inquiry some months afterward. "It was at once apparent that instead of the cables in the main span rising and falling together, they were moving in opposite directions, thereby tilting the deck from side to side."

Eldridge walked out onto the bridge for a closer look. He crossed the east span, which was still fairly quiet, and went a quarter of the way onto the main span. He saw that the concrete sidewalk was beginning to crack, though not the automobile roadway. The span was twisting in a kind of corkscrew motion, now one side tilting, now the other. He began hopefully to plan a system of bracing cables that could be installed later in the day, if the wind died down.

The wind did not die down. A floor panel in the center of the span broke loose and fell to the water. Then, just before 11 A.M., the steel hangers that connected the roadway to the suspension cables began to snap. As Eldridge watched in dismay from the toll plaza, a big section of steel dropped out of the span. More hangers snapped, flying high in the air and twanging like piano strings.

A 600-foot section of the main span ripped free and went crashing down. For a moment, the bridge was still, as though steadying itself after enduring this frightful wound. Then the wild rhythmic convulsions returned. The rest of Galloping Gertie's main span plunged into the water. With the balancing weight of the central span gone, the two side spans rose abruptly, then fell. Thousands of tons of steel spilled into the water, sending up a dome-like splash of white.

The disintegration of the bridge was complete. Galloping Gertie had perished.

No lives had been lost, but millions of dollars had been wasted. Newspapers throughout the country the next day showed dramatic, terrifying photographs of the fall of the bridge. Never had so big a bridge collapsed before. Never had the death-throes been so astounding.

Why had Galloping Gertie fallen?

In the immediate aftermath of the catastrophe, no one could really say, and that was perhaps the most frightening aspect of the whole event. The bridge had broken up in a wind of only 42 miles per hour, far below its designed strength. If that could happen, how safe were the other slender new suspension bridges? What of the George Washington, which had no truss at all? What of the Golden Gate? What of the Bronx-Whitestone, second only to Galloping Gertie in slimness and length? Was it only a matter of luck that had kept those bridges standing thus far?

In the general agitation, no one was more upset than the professional bridge engineers. They feared for their own works, and began to ask themselves harsh questions. The fact that no less a man than Leon Moisseiff had built the fallen bridge was sobering to contemplate—for if he could make such a huge mistake, anyone could.

The public authority that had sponsored the Tacoma-Narrows Bridge appointed a three-man commission to study the collapse and draw conclusions that would make other suspension bridges safer.

This spectacular photo was taken as a large section of the concrete roadway in the center span of the new Tacoma-Narrows Bridge hurtled into Puget Sound, Nov. 7, 1940. High winds caused the bridge to sway and undulate and finally crack under the strain.

The commission consisted of Glenn Woodruff, one of the planners of the Golden Gate and Bay suspension bridges; Theodore von Karman of the California Institute of Technology, an expert on wind forces; and the veteran bridge engineer, Othmar H. Ammann. They examined the site, looked at the newsreel photos of Galloping Gertie's last moments, and issued their report at the end of March, 1941.

The fall of the bridge, they said, had not resulted from anything so simple as a high wind's merely knocking the structure down. Only a super-hurricane could have done that. Rather, the extreme lightness and flexibility of the big bridge had left it vulnerable to oscillations, or flutterings. The bridge had fluttered like a flag in a breeze. But concrete and steel cannot resist such twisting oscillations for long. The motions had caused a cable band to slip free, and that permitted ever more violent oscillations that had at last ripped the deck apart. While such oscillations had been seen on other bridges—the deck of the Golden Gate, in 1938, had rippled in waves two feet high under the impact of a wind velocity of 62 miles an hour—the Tacoma-Narrows Bridge, because of its unique proportions, had been far more susceptible to such forces. The three engineers called for "further study" of wind effects before any other suspension bridges were built with such a high ratio of width to length.

About the same time, an engineer who had not been appointed to the panel of experts was issuing a report of his own. He was David Steinman of New York, who held forceful opinions on many subjects and was not shy about airing them. Steinman had designed a long, slender suspension bridge himself in 1938, the Thousand Islands Bridge between New York State and Canada. Like the ill-fated Tacoma-Narrows Bridge, it had been stiffened only by a shallow plate girder; and it, too, had gone into troublesome vertical heaving motions in a strong wind.

Steinman had made a quick guess about the trouble. Almost always in the history of bridge-building, engineers have coped with the unusual by a process of intuitive guesswork, with the mathematical theory coming later. Steinman decided that rigid stays running from the plate girders to the suspension cables would keep his bridge stable. The stays were installed just a few days before President Roosevelt and the Prime Minister of Canada were to dedicate the bridge. There were no further problems of oscillation on the Thousand Islands Bridge.

Two years later, when the Tacoma-Narrows Bridge was nearing completion and already showing signs of an unhealthy wobble, Steinman wrote to Leon Moiseiff, offering to explain his system of stays. Moiseiff politely declined Steinman's help. A few months afterward it became necessary to install stays on Galloping Gertie anyway, and, Steinman charged, the engineers had borrowed his idea without really understanding it. They had used stays of wire rope, and so had Steinman. But, he wrote:

"They did not know that the wire-rope mid-span stays on the Thousand Islands Bridge were only an emergency, a temporary installation that we replaced a few months later by the permanent stays made of rigid structural-steel angle members. Even so, the mid-span stays at Tacoma, copied from me, although inadequate, were the only thing that kept the bridge from going into destructive oscillations during the four months of its life. On the fatal morning, one of the rope-stays became slack and snapped, whereupon the span went into its dance of death. . . . If they had let me help them, I could have saved the bridge, as I have saved several other bridges. I could have made the Tacoma span safe for a very small expenditure. But my offer went begging."

Steinman's blunt, uncompromising words angered a number of other engineers, who felt that he was being too harsh on Moisseiff and somewhat too complimentary toward himself. The three-man investigating commission went to the trouble of pointing out that the Thousand Islands Bridge was actually five separate bridges, including two suspension spans, and that each of these spans was much smaller than Galloping Gertie. "They give no clue to the possible behavior of a suspension bridge 3½ times longer and 6 times heavier," the commission declared, partially justifying Moisseiff's lack of interest in Steinman's offer of advice. Steinman himself later withdrew some of his remarks, admitting that neither he nor Moisseiff nor anyone else had really understood much in 1940 about the response of a huge, narrow suspension bridge to wind forces. Only the violent death of Galloping Gertie had provided some insight into those forces.

The lesson of Galloping Gertie led to some rapid modifications of existing suspension bridges. The Bronx-Whitestone Bridge, which was most nearly similar to the Tacoma-Narrows in general dimensions, received diagonal wind stays and then a deep stiffening truss. The Golden Gate Bridge was reinforced, at a cost of $3,500,000. Bridges then on the drawing boards were redesigned to include strong trusses. The Washington Toll Bridge Authority announced that it would build a new Tacoma-Narrows span, and all thoughts of slimness were forgotten. The new bridge, which was completed in 1950, used the original piers and approaches of Galloping Gertie, but its deck was 60 feet wide instead of 39, and carried four traffic lanes. Stiffening trusses 33 feet high took the place of the 8-foot-high plate girders of the fallen bridge. They provided 37 times as much stiffness. As a further attempt to lessen wind effects, a number of open slots were left in the roadway between the traffic lanes.

The engineering profession was gentle toward the unhappy Leon Moisseiff. When the Tay Bridge had fallen in 1879, the engineering career of Thomas Bouch collapsed with it. The demise of the Quebec Bridge in 1907 destroyed the career of Theodore Cooper. But in 1940 most engineers realized that Moisseiff's bad luck could have struck any one of them—that the whole profession had been building in the dark, and it was only his ill fortune to have one of his bridges so vividly demonstrate the faults of all. He was defended in the professional journals, and after his death, some years later, a fund was set up for an annual Moisseiff Award, given by the American Society of Civil Engineers for the year's most important paper on structural design.

It happened, though, that at the time of the Tacoma disaster Leon Moisseiff held a contract for another large suspension bridge. This was a span crossing the Strait of Mackinac in Michigan. Moisseiff's design called for a handsome, slender bridge stiffened only by a shallow plate girder. Construction work had already begun.

The state of Michigan found itself in a nasty dilemma. Could it let Moisseiff go ahead with the bridge now? Would the public be willing to use a Moisseiff-designed bridge? Even though the engineering profession had risen to his defense, Moisseiff's reputation was considerably tarnished in the eyes of laymen. What to do?

The bombing of Pearl Harbor in December, 1941, provided a convenient excuse to shelve the whole project. The United States was at war, and new bridges would have to wait while guns and battleships were produced. After the war, the Mackinac project was revived—minus Moiseiff. The Michigan legislature required a three-man board of engineers to be named to design an entirely different Mackinac Bridge.

The engineers were chosen. They included two powerful figures who cordially disliked each other: Othmar Ammann and David Steinman. Glenn Woodruff, of the San Francisco bridges, was the third man. This ill-assorted trio was given the job of building one of history's biggest bridges, and the ghost that haunted everyone was the ghost of Galloping Gertie.

11:

An Era of Giant Bridges

The Mackinac Straits Bridge

THE STATE OF MICHIGAN IS ACTUALLY TWO SEPARATE PENINSULAS. Lower Michigan, shaped like a mittened hand, juts northward between Lake Michigan and Lake Huron, and carries most of the state's population. Detroit, Lansing, Saginaw, Battle Creek, and the other major cities of Michigan are all on this peninsula. Above it, spearing from west to east, is Upper Michigan, a sparsely settled district where hunters revel in the wild forests. The wide Strait of Mackinac splits the two unequal sections of the state.

Undeveloped, unvisited, Upper Michigan had long been a kind of stepchild area. For decades there had been talk of building a bridge across the strait, but nothing had ever come of such talk. The distance to be spanned was more than five miles; the howling winds that roared through the strait would administer savage punishment to any bridge; the giant ice floes of Michigan's brutal winters would menace piers and foundations.

Leon Moisseiff's design called for a composite bridge—long approaches leading to a high suspension span. When the project was revived after the war, the same basic scheme was used, but with significant differences. Since the Tacoma disaster, slender

The Mackinac Bridge is of a composite design—long approaches leading to a high suspension span.

suspension bridges had ceased to be fashionable. The Mackinac Bridge was going to be big in every respect.

It should have been obvious from the start that no three-man commission including both David Steinman and Othmar Ammann was ever going to produce a bridge. These two great engineers, both forceful and dynamic and formidably competent, had competed with one another for major bridge contracts for forty years, and the relationship between them was something less than cordial. Steinman, born in 1886, was seven years younger than Ammann, and disagreed with him on just about every major and minor point of bridge-building. Their personalities clashed, too. The Swiss Ammann tended to be reserved, soft-spoken, quietly modest. Steinman, a native New Yorker, never hid his feelings and was often brash in setting forth his views.

The third man on the panel, Glenn Woodruff, was hard put to keep the tempers of the two titans under control. Finally Ammann withdrew from the job entirely, and David Steinman was picked to design the bridge alone.

Work began early in the 1950's. To guard against the danger of ice floes, Steinman put down mammoth foundations for his piers—nearly a million tons of concrete. The towers for the suspension span rose 552 feet above the strait. In November, 1955, with the towers not yet completely riveted together, a 76-mile-per-hour gale struck the unfinished bridge, sending giant masses of ice careening into the foundations. The towers were unharmed—a measure of the great strength Steinman gave them.

The suspension bridge has a span of 3,800 feet, which at the time made it the second longest in the world, exceeded only by the Golden Gate. Besides this tower-to-tower span, the cables run thousands of feet further to their anchorages, for an overall cable length of 8,344 feet. These are still the longest suspension bridge cables in the world. Mindful of the fate of Galloping Gertie, Steinman braced his bridge against the winds of the strait with trusses 38 feet high. Certain novel features in the placement of these trusses were intended to give additional protection against the wind.

The approaches to this suspension span are truss bridges, one of them a 2,082-foot span that is the world's longest continuous truss unit. Including these approaches, the bridge runs 5.4 miles. It cost $100,000,000 to construct.

The Mackinac Bridge was designed to resist the worst that the elements could offer, and since its completion in 1958 it has shown its durability again and again. From its foundations, resting on bedrock more than 200 feet below the surface of the strait, to the tops of its lofty towers, it stands as staunchly as its designer intended.

It was David Steinman's farewell to bridge-building. He had two other great enterprises in mind, but he lost one to his rival Othmar Ammann, and the other was snatched from him by time itself. It was Ammann, as we shortly will see, who drew the assignment to build the Verrazano-Narrows Bridge across New York Harbor, though Steinman had hoped to be chosen. Steinman had also hoped to build the Messina Straits Bridge in Italy, with a main suspension span of more than 5,000 feet. But death called him in 1960, and the Messina Straits Bridge is still unbuilt.

The Chesapeake Bay Bridge-Tunnel

Not all the great bridges of recent years are suspensions. Not all have record-breaking spans. Not all have been built in water so deep that they taxed human ingenuity to the limit. The Chesapeake Bay Bridge-Tunnel, which is as long and as complicated as its own name, is a great engineering accomplishment even though none of its many sections is of extraordinary size itself.

The bridge-tunnel, as it must be called, opened for traffic in the spring of 1964. Its purpose was to connect Virginia's isolated Eastern Shore area to the rest of the state by spanning the mouth of Chesapeake Bay. This 17.6-mile distance was the last major gap in a coastal highway route running from Canada to Florida. Trucks and autos taking the shore route before the building of the bridge-tunnel were required to make a 90-minute ferry ride across the bay, often with long waiting times between ferries. Now the crossing can be made in 20 to 30 minutes, with no waiting time at all.

Naturally, a 17.6-mile bay crossing cannot be achieved in a single structure. The $200,000,000 bridge-tunnel has many parts.

Leaving the mainland Virginia shore at Virginia Beach, it snakes across 3.3 miles of shallow water as a low-level trestle supported by concrete legs. Then it vanishes from sight, swooping down into a mile-long tunnel on the floor of the bay. Reappearing, it runs along another low trestle for 3.75 miles, before entering a second mile-long tunnel. Once more the road surfaces for four and a half additional miles of trestle, leading to a steel arch bridge seven-tenths of a mile in length; then it becomes a causeway angling over an island one and one-half miles wide, turns into a short trestle again, then another bridge, and a final trestle a tenth of a mile long that carries the road to the shore.

It sounds complex, and it certainly is. The needs of navigation and even those of fishermen were taken into account when the crossing was planned. The problem was to build the most economical possible roadway, while still leaving the important Chesapeake Bay shipping lanes unblocked. The answer took the form of an assortment of trestles, tunnels, arch bridges, and man-made islands, all put together by some of the strangest equipment ever used in construction work.

The highest point on the 17.6-mile crossing of Chesapeake Bay Bridge-Tunnel is the North Channel Bridge which provides 75 feet of vertical clearance for fishing vessels on the Atlantic Ocean (shown here under construction).

Much of the bay is no more than 30 feet deep. That meant that more than a dozen miles of the course could be bridged in the simplest possible way, by driving a great many concrete piles into the bottom and placing short spans from pile to pile. That would form what one writer has called "a seagoing centipede" that walks "on hundreds of concrete legs."

However, the two navigation channels in the middle of the bay caused special considerations. Any bridge built there would have to be high enough to let big ships pass beneath. The city of Baltimore, whose port would be affected by any Chesapeake Bay bridging, objected to the whole idea, on the grounds that it didn't want to have to set restrictions on the height and width of ships that called there. The U.S. Navy also raised an argument; in case of an enemy bombing attack that destroyed the bridges, the shallow bay would be blocked by the wreckage.

The chief engineer, Percy Michener, had to weigh these arguments carefully. Michener, born in 1904, had a wide experience in engineering; since his graduation from engineering school in 1926 he had built bridges, pipelines, highways, tunnels, and a 324-mile railroad in Saudi Arabia. This was his biggest assignment, though. For many months, he surveyed not only the currents of the bay and the condition of the bottom, but also local political problems and the financial feasibility of the whole project. At last, he scrapped his original plan to build high-level bridges over the navigation channels, and decided on a pair of tunnels instead, thus leaving the mile-wide channels totally clear.

The fishermen had their objections too. Fishing is not only a sport but a major industry in the Chesapeake Bay region. The long miles of low trestles would form a wall across the bay, the roadway running so close to the water that fishing boats could not pass below it. Fishermen chasing a school of fish near the Eastern Shore would have to make a detour of many miles to get around the trestle. To accommodate them, Michener agreed to build two bridges flanking Fisherman Island near the Eastern Shore, an important fishing ground. Fishermen and yachtsmen would be able to get through under the high bridges without having to go all the way to the mid-bay navigation channels.

Work began in September, 1960. Two pairs of man-made islands had to be constructed as entrance and exit points for the mid-bay tunnels. North and South Islands were built flanking the site of the Thimble Shoal Channel Tunnel; East and West Islands, four miles to the northeast, rose as the boundaries of the companion Chesapeake Channel Tunnel. Hydraulic dredges piled up heaps of sand on the bottom of the bay, nearly 100 feet below the surface. Gravel, rock, and finally huge boulders were placed on this sandy foundation until the artificial islands cleared the water by 30 feet. The trestles, when they were built, would carry the roadway to these islands, where it would plunge in a steady slope to the tunnel below.

The tunnels were prefabricated ones. Double-walled cylinders 100 yards long, sealed at both ends, were built in Texas and towed 2,000 miles to Chesapeake Bay. At a dock in Norfolk, Virginia, the space between the two steel shells was filled with concrete until the cylinders were nearly submerged in the water. Concrete also was poured through hatches in the cylinder roofing to form the roadbed of the future tunnels. Meanwhile, a shallow trench was being dredged along the floor of the bay. When the cylinders were ready, they were towed to the exact tunnel site and filled with the last few tons of concrete needed to sink them to the bottom. Deep-sea divers guided the cylinders into their positions in the trench at low tide. The final step was to cut away the end plates and link the joined sections into a single tunnel. Each tunnel was composed of 19 such sections, welded together so that there would be no leaks.

The biggest part of the job was installing the dozen-plus miles of trestle-carried roadway. Though this was done in shallow water, frequent storms turned the water rough and made the process a complicated one. Bizarre and gigantic machines were devised to lay the 2,640 concrete piles of the long trestles.

The floor of Chesapeake Bay is mud and sediment, as deep as 2,500 feet in some places. Driving piles to bedrock is impossible there. To insure the stability of a trestle bridge founded in muck, the piles had to be driven as much as 100 feet down, which called for special equipment. A monstrous pile-driving machine called

A workman watches as the specially designed pile driver, called "Big D," drives a giant pile into the bottom of the Chesapeake Bay to support the Bridge-Tunnel's trestled roadway. Four and a half feet in diameter, the piles ranged in length from 60 feet to 172 feet.

"the Big D" got the job. The Big D was a platform standing on stilt-like legs long enough to reach to the bottom of the bay. Striding out into the water, it took up a position where the surveyors said a pile had to be driven. Then it grasped one of the concrete piles, which were as much as 172 feet long, and with ferocious hammer-blows pounded it into the muddy bottom. When the pile was in place, the Big D's legs were pulled up and it marched forward to lay the next.

In the wake of the Big D came an equally strange device that won the nickname of "the Two-headed Monster." The task of the Monster was to lop off the tops of the piles so they all stood at the same level, and then to cap each group of three piles with a 40-ton slab of reinforced concrete that would serve as the end support for a span of the trestle. Actually, the Two-headed Monster was a kind of bridge itself, a traveling platform mounted on a steel track. Huge arms descended from the platform and grasped for the three pile groups that the Big D had driven. Supporting itself on two groups of piles at a time, the Two-headed Monster would reach a crane forward to snip a third set of piles to a level height. At the same time, a second crane in the rear of the platform would be capping a fourth set of piles. When the front group was leveled and the rear group was capped, the Monster would heave itself forward on its own steel track, advancing to the next group of piles. Slowly it crawled out across the bay, keeping close behind the pile-driving Big D.

A third giant, called "the Slab-setter," came along behind the Two-headed Monster to put down the roadbed. The Slab-setter was a huge crane on a 150-foot framework. The framework rested on the capped piles. The arm of the crane reached out and lifted

Stretching off into the horizon are the "three-legged" piles that support the trestled roadway which, along with two tunnels, four man-made islands and two bridges, constitute the Chesapeake Bay Bridge-Tunnel. In the background is the "Two-headed Monster."

concrete slabs from a barge nearby. These 75-foot slabs were set in place from one pile capping to the next. When four slabs were laid side by side from cap to cap, a 75-foot section of the trestle was complete. Then the Slab-setter would roll forward 75 feet to the front half of its own framework. The crane would swing around, pick up the rear half of the framework, pivot, and put it down over the next set of caps. Now the process began again—hoist the slabs, put them in place, roll forward on the just-completed roadbed, pick up the rear section of the framework and move it forward, and hoist another slab.

Methodically the three monsters made their way across the bay, driving piles, leveling and capping them, installing the roadbed. In March, 1962, the steady rhythm of the job was interrupted by a storm well remembered all along the Atlantic coast. High winds and raging tides buffeted beaches for more than a thousand miles. The Big D reared up on its stilt-like legs to get above the surging water, but the fury of the storm toppled the $1,500,000 rig and hurled it into the bay. Helicopters rescued the workmen clinging to the wreckage, but there was no way to salvage the pile driver. A second Big D had to be constructed, delaying completion of the trestle by many months.

In time the trestle was completed and the roadway was paved. The tunnels were finished and given their lining of glistening tile. The steel arch bridges near the Eastern Shore area were laid in place. "It isn't only a question of building a bridge *over* the water," an engineer commented as the elaborate complex neared completion. "We're building this bridge *on* the water, *in* the water, and *through* the water."

On April 15, 1964, amid great predictions of new prosperity for the region it would serve, the Chesapeake Bay Bridge-Tunnel was officially opened. There was talk of adding a second section in a few years' time, a 10-mile trestle carrying the bridge from the Eastern Shore to Hampton, Virginia. But in its first eighteen months of service, the bridge-tunnel produced a surprise for its financial backers. Despite the convenience of the much-heralded bay crossing, traffic was unexpectedly light. Toll revenue was so low that it became a problem for the bridge authority to pay the interest on the money it had borrowed for construction. The engineering calculations were perfect—but not the monetary ones. It may be quite a while before the Hampton extension is built.

The Verrazano-Narrows Bridge

Most men who are lucky enough to live to the age of eighty-five are content to sit quietly on the sidelines, leaving hard chores to the youngsters. Not Othmar Ammann. He celebrated his eighty-fifth birthday in March, 1964, and the following November found him attending the dedication ceremonies of his last and greatest bridge, the monumental Verrazano-Narrows span in New York Harbor.

As chief engineer of the Port of New York Authority, Ammann had placed a permanent imprint on the history of his profession with the George Washington Bridge. At the age of sixty, he left the employment of the Port Authority, not to retire but to found his own engineering firm, Ammann & Whitney. The new firm built airports in Ethiopia and in Washington, D.C.; it built a highway system in Iran; it helped build the Pittsburgh Civic Arena. It put the lower deck on the George Washington Bridge. And it received the coveted Verrazano-Narrows assignment.

So far as the technique of bridge-building goes, there is nothing special about the Verrazano-Narrows Bridge. The basic principle of the steel cable suspension bridge was established by the Roeblings in the 19th century. The George Washington, Golden Gate, and Mackinac Bridges all showed that it was possible to build such a bridge with a span greater than 3,500 feet. The Verrazano-Narrows Bridge did not depart in any significant way from the pattern set by those bridges. It is merely a little bigger.

The statistics of the bridge are awesome. Ammann let a few records remain for the older bridges, but only a few. The length of its cables—7,205 feet—is more than 1,100 feet less than the cable length of the Mackinac Bridge. The 690-foot-high towers are nearly sixty feet shorter than those of the Golden Gate Bridge. The road-way—103 feet wide—is three feet narrower than the roadway of the George Washington Bridge.

But——

From tower to tower, the span of the bridge is 4,260 feet, a new record by 60 feet. The towers are so far apart that in planning them Ammann had to take into account the curvature of the earth's surface; they are one and five-eighths inches farther apart at top than at bottom. The four steel cables, each three feet in diameter, are strong enough to support the weight of an ocean liner. Those cables cost more than the whole Golden Gate Bridge, while the overall price tag for the Verrazano-Narrows Bridge was $325,000,000. Into the bridge went 188,000 tons of steel—three times as much as was used to build the Empire State Building. The bridge is huge, and it is beautiful, for Ammann had remarked, "It is a crime to build an ugly bridge." Spanning the gateway to New York Harbor, the big bridge will be the first glimpse of America for those who come here by sea.

The first voyager from Europe to glimpse that harbor was Giovanni da Verrazano, who arrived in 1524. He sailed through the opening between the shores of what are now Brooklyn and Staten Island, and entered the wide, magnificent harbor of the future New York. Millions of voyagers came after Verrazano, all passing through the mile-wide strait known as the Narrows, between Upper and Lower New York Bay. Settlements along the shores became towns, and the towns became cities. By 1888, there were plans for a tunnel under the Narrows from Brooklyn to Staten Island, but nothing was done. In 1923, excavations for such a tunnel actually were begun, only to be abandoned almost at once.

Then came the dream of a Narrows Bridge. Once the George Washington Bridge was built, it became clear that the Narrows too could be spanned. The immense cost of the project kept it only a dream for 20 years. By 1950, however, the press of traffic through tiny Manhattan Island had begun to strangle the city. New highways carried hordes of automobiles through the northeastern United States; but any car going from New England or Long Island to New Jersey or Pennsylvania had to go through the narrow island of Manhattan. A bridge across New York Harbor would permit traffic to be routed through Brooklyn into Staten Island, which already was connected by bridge to the New Jersey mainland. The hub of the city could be bypassed.

View of Staten Island anchorage of the Verrazano-Narrows Bridge under construction, showing cables.

For seven years more, the city planners asked themselves whether the crossing should be made by bridge or by tunnel, and at last decided on a bridge. It was not a popular decision in some places. Thousands of homes would have to be demolished in Brooklyn to make way for the bridge approaches. And the people of Staten Island, happy in their woodsy isolation from the rest of the city, did not relish the thought of a sudden deluge of automobiles. The loud outcry of protest gave the project an uneasy sendoff.

Even choosing a name for the proposed bridge caused picketing at City Hall. The original idea of calling it simply the Narrows Bridge was quickly scuttled when a group called the Italian Historical Society recommended naming the bridge for Giovanni da

Verrazano. The city officials, unwilling to offend millions of Italian-American voters, seemed willing to accept the suggestion. But other groups of voters spoke up also in favor of such names as the Staten Island Bridge, the New World Bridge, the Freedom Bridge, and the Gateway Bridge. After months of debate, a name was selected: the Verrazano-Narrows Bridge.

At that point someone noticed that the explorer had spelled his name with a double z, according to some authorities, but there was only one z in the name of the bridge! More arguing followed. Was it to be "Verrazzano" or "Verrazano"? Scholars offered conflicting opinions. The dispute took on mystifying political overtones. When all the smoke of battle cleared, the single-z spelling was triumphant.

Othmar Ammann took no part in all these uproars. He and his firm were busy with underwater investigations, soil studies, surveys, design sketches. By January, 1960, construction began on the foundations for the two 27,000-ton towers.

It would not be possible to rest these foundations on bedrock. A floor of firm sand and clay would be used. On the Brooklyn side, the foundation would reach 170 feet below the water surface, and the Staten Island foundation would be 105 feet down.

The two caissons for these foundations were the largest ever built: 229 feet long and 129 feet wide. Each had 66 holes seventeen feet in diameter in it, so that, as a newspaper reporter put it, "from a distance the concrete caissons looked like gigantic chunks of Swiss cheese."

The caissons were moved into position, and cranes equipped with dredging buckets began to haul muck and sand up through the holes. Slowly the caissons settled into a level attitude. As they sank, new courses of concrete were poured on top so the work could continue without going to great depths. During the 26 months of this phase of the construction, more than 81,000 cubic yards of muck were dredged up on the Staten Island side, and 47,000 cubic yards of concrete went into the caisson. On the Brooklyn side, 143,600 cubic yards of muck were removed, and 83,000 cubic yards of concrete poured.

In October, 1960, work started on the two anchorages for the cables. These, erected behind each tower on the shore, were blocks of concrete the size of 10-story buildings. They would have to hold back the 240,000,000-pound pull of the cables.

The towers and the anchorages were completed by November, 1962. Giant derricks with lifting capacities of more than 100 tons had crawled up the sides of the towers on special tracks, lifting section after section in place. When they were finished, the spinning of the cables could begin.

First, as always, came the construction of the temporary platforms on which the workmen would stand. A barge dragged the first rope across the Narrows, and derricks on top of the two towers hoisted it from the water. Other ropes followed, until a dozen strands of wire, two inches thick and more than a mile long, stretched from anchorage to anchorage. On these the two catwalks were fastened—a pair of giant wire mesh hammocks, twenty feet wide across the entire span of the bridge. With these in place, the workmen strung another set of wires fifteen feet above each catwalk. These were to carry the four traveling wheels that would spin the cables.

The double-grooved wheels, four feet in diameter and weighing several hundred pounds, carried two wires at once, and two wheels at a time ran above each catwalk. Diesel engines mounted on the anchorages powered them to a speed of eight miles an hour, thirteen miles an hour on the downhill slopes. Workmen stationed along the catwalk from point to point grabbed the wires and hooked them in place as the wheels went by. When each wheel reached the anchorage on the far side, it was taken down, reloaded with wire, and sent back on a new trip.

Every 428 wires made up one strand. There were 61 strands to the cable. That was 26,018 wires per cable, clamped together by powerful hydraulic jacks. The four cables weigh 39,000 tons, and contain a total of 142,500 miles of wire. From these cables would be suspended the steel hangers, up to 447 feet long, that were to carry the road deck.

It took nearly six months to spin the cables. Back and forth zipped the wheels, each work gang trying to outdo the next. One crew managed to run 50 round trips in a single work shift; a few

View of north catwalk of Staten Island side span of the Verrazano-Narrows
Bridge, showing installation of temporary electric cable in progress.

weeks later the record was pushed to 51, and then to 53. Once a wheel broke loose and nearly ran down one of the workmen, but he jumped aside just in time. The spinning, which had started in March, 1963, lasted until October.

Meanwhile, in an assembly yard in Jersey City, the steel sections of the roadway were being built. Each of these weighed 388 tons. Barges carried them to the bridge site to be hoisted into place and fastened to the hangers. This was the most dangerous part of the work for the men; and, just as it was about to begin, a young construction man slipped from a cable and fell to his death.

He was the third to die on the bridge. In August, 1962, a man had fallen from a ladder during the building of the towers. In the summer of 1963, another man slipped while working on the approach road. This third death, coming only days before the most grueling part of the job, hurt morale badly. Some of the men, nervous now, asked that safety nets be installed under the catwalks, but the request was turned down by the bridge-building company.

The hoisting of the deck began.

The central span went up first—60 pieces, each 28 feet high, 115 feet wide, and nearly as long. They had to be lifted more than 220 feet in the air and attached to the hangers. If any piece dropped into the water, it would mean a six-month delay while a replacement was forged.

As each deck section was attached, it exerted a downward pull on the cables. The first section drew them down 20 inches; the second and third pieces pulled them another four feet six inches. All this had been part of Ammann's calculations; when all the sections were in place, the cables would be drawn down more than 28 feet to their final curve.

On November 21, 1963, while this work was going on, the hoisting engine conked out and a 388-ton section that was halfway up had to be left dangling in mid-air overnight. The next day, the jittery workmen corrected the engine trouble and put the dangling piece in place. Later that day came the terrible news from Dallas that President Kennedy had been assassinated. Many of the workmen were Irish-Americans who took the death of the young President as a family tragedy. Nerves were strained to the breaking-

Brooklyn view of the Verrazano-Narrows Bridge under construction, showing cable wrapping machine, and men on south catwalk.

point, and there was fear that some of the edgier men might fall to their deaths. All the next week, there was renewed muttering about safety nets. The bridge company still did not want to install them. Safety nets could cover only a small part of the bridge site, since the road sections had to be hoisted through the path of any nets. And, as the Golden Gate construction had shown, even nets did not necessarily provide safety.

The men insisted. On December 2, they went out on strike, and all work halted for four days. Then the company yielded and nets were strung. It proved to be a good idea, too; three men fell off the bridge in 1964 and all were saved by the nets. By spring, the last of the heavy steel sections was in place. Now came the less spectacular task of joining them, tightening the bolts, paving a roadway over the steel deck, stringing up the lights, painting the cables to protect them against the rain. On November 21, 1964, brass bands played, ribbons were cut, and the biggest bridge of all was dedicated after a swift five years of work.

A parade of limousines brought the high officials to the Brooklyn entrance of the bridge: Governor Rockefeller of New York State; Mayor Wagner of New York City; Cardinal Spellman, the Archbishop of New York; the presidents of the boroughs linked by the bridge; and many other dignitaries. During the ribbon-cutting ceremony, a lean, elderly man in a blue coat and a blue muffler stood quietly to one side, looking at the bridge. Few people recog-

General view from Brooklyn of the completed Verrazano-Narrows Bridge.

nized him. One who did was a newspaperman who asked, "How do you feel, Mr. Ammann?"

"Oh," he said, "as I feel every day."

The 52 shiny black limousines moved slowly across the bridge to the Staten Island side for more ceremonies. Othmar Ammann did not make any speech. The master of ceremonies pointed to him in the grandstand and asked him to rise. He stood up, removing his hat, and nodded to the applause. "It may be that in the midst of so many celebrities, you don't even know who he is," the master of ceremonies declared. "My friends, I ask that you now look upon the greatest living bridge engineer, perhaps the greatest of all time." But the master of ceremonies forgot to mention Othmar Ammann's name.

Less than a year later, in September, 1965, Ammann died at the age of eighty-six. Few New Yorkers know his name; but the bridges that are his monuments are known to all.

12:

Bridges
Of Tomorrow

IF ANYTHING IS CERTAIN IN THE WORLD OF THE BRIDGE-BUILDERS, it is that tomorrow will bring bold new developments. Ever bigger bridges, new methods of construction—these are sure to come.

Probably the rate of progress will not seem so rapid as it was about 1800 and again about 1880. The shift from the age-old custom of building bridges from stone to building them from iron was a real engineering revolution, which had great effects on the size and design of bridges. The coming of steel eighty years later produced another upheaval in bridge design. No such dramatic changes seem to be on the horizon today—only steady refinements of present techniques.

By the same token, increases in bridge size are likely to be frequent but not startling in terms of percentage. When Othmar Ammann's George Washington Bridge was completed in 1931, its span was nearly twice as great as the next biggest bridge of that time. To repeat such a jump today, some engineer would have to design and build a bridge with a 9,000-foot span. The 9,000-foot bridge will doubtless come, but only after bridges of 5,000 and 6,000 and 7,000 and 8,000 feet have been erected.

Some of the changes in bridge design have already made themselves felt. The concrete pontoon bridge, a modern version of the floating bridges of antiquity, has recently attained great size. Two colossal floating bridges across Lake Washington near Seattle each have more than 6,500 feet of concrete pontoons. In Portugal, a suspension bridge was built with two highly unusual caissons: one was deliberately warped at the bottom to fit an uneven rockbed, and the other, at a depth of 260 feet below water level, is the deepest ever placed. New design techniques such as the *delta girder* and the *orthotropic deck* have permitted substantial reductions in the quantity of steel needed for conventional bridges.

Sometimes the experiments fail. In 1963, the John Day Bridge in Oregon was put in place over the Columbia River. It was made of six different grades of steel, including a special, newly devised high-strength heat-treated steel. There were six 200-foot truss spans and four 80-foot welded spans. The steelwork of this bridge was hailed by engineers as an example of the most modern design techniques. But when the John Day Bridge was a year old, the waters of a flood caused one of its supporting concrete piers to fail. Two of the 200-foot spans collapsed into the river.

So long as bridge-builders are human and the elements are merciless, there will always be such disasters. But the new steels and the perfection of reinforced concrete are contributing to bigger, stronger, and safer bridges all the time. It would be pointless even to try to make a list of the biggest bridges of the world by type, because most of the list would be out of date before this book saw print. Some records are likely to stand a long time, like the one for the longest stone arch bridge, set in 1903 in Germany. No one is building long stone arch bridges today. But the present records for suspension, concrete arch, girder, truss, and cantilever bridges are likely to be eclipsed within the next few years, and then eclipsed again.

Some remarkably ambitious bridge projects are in the design and planning stage now. They may be under construction soon— or they may be delayed ten or twenty years as practical considerations interfere. Let us glance briefly at the plans for some of these bridges of tomorrow.

The Long Island Sound Bridge

Long Island Sound is a lengthy body of water separating the northern shore of Long Island from the southern shores of Connecticut and Rhode Island. As population grows in Nassau and Suffolk Counties in eastern Long Island, demand has increased for a bridge across Long Island Sound that would permit cars to reach New England without the need to make a trip of up to 100 miles into New York City.

A bridge has been proposed to run from Orient Point at Long Island's eastern tip to Fisher's Island in the sound, and from there to Napatree Point, Rhode Island. The overall length of the bridge would be 23.8 miles, making it the second longest bridge in the United States, counting low-level trestle sections. The cost of such a bridge would be immense, and it has not entirely been welcomed by the communities it would serve. The proposal is still under study and no decision is likely for several years. Right now the crossing is made by ferry.

Another Long Island Sound Bridge has been proposed at the opposite end of the island, close to New York City. This one would run from Long Island to Westchester County, New York. While the people of Long Island and those of Westchester are eager to have a bridge that would allow traffic to cross the sound without going into New York City, no community is particularly happy to have the bridge in its own territory, and at the present time the project has been put aside.

The Humber River Bridge

A proposed suspension bridge over the Humber River near Hull, England, would have a main span of record length—4,580 feet. This would exceed the span of the Verrazano-Narrows Bridge by 320 feet. The Humber River Bridge would be much more slender than the Verrazano-Narrows—four traffic lanes instead of twelve—and its estimated cost of $35,000,000 would be only about a tenth as great. An unusual deck and suspending hanger design, making use of six-sided box girders instead of conventional stiffening trusses, is expected to reduce both the weight and the cost of this bridge, when and if it is built.

The Tokyo Bay Bridge

Early in 1965, the Japanese Ministry of Construction began making surveys for two giant suspension bridges. One, across the Akashi Strait near the city of Kobe, would have a main span of 4,265 feet—five feet longer than that of the Verrazano-Narrows Bridge. The other, across the mouth of Tokyo Bay, would have a total length of almost five miles and a suspended central span of about 4,900 feet. This bridge, with six lanes for traffic, would connect with a proposed eight-lane, 93-mile highway to encircle Tokyo Bay.

The Messina Straits Bridge

Since 1870, Italians have dreamed of a bridge across the Strait of Messina, the body of water that separates the toe of the Italian "boot" from the large island of Sicily. The engineering problems are formidable. Fierce currents and whirlpools sweep through the strait. In his *Odyssey*, Homer turned the whirlpools into hideous monsters, Scylla and Charybdis, that menaced all seamen who passed through the strait. The strong currents have cut great irregularities into the bottom of the strait, creating difficulties for bridge-builders. Earthquakes are frequent in the area. Heavy gales rake the strait several times a year.

One of David Steinman's last projects, before his death in 1960, was a proposal for a suspension bridge with a 5,000-foot main span across the strait. He devised a special method of wind bracing to give his bridge rigidity. Today, fifteen Italian companies and several American engineering firms are working together on preliminary studies for such a bridge, which would have the world's longest suspension span. Its piers would have to go down nearly 450 feet below the surface of the strait, far deeper than the foundations of any other bridge.

The engineering firms hired the famed undersea explorer, Jacques-Yves Cousteau, to survey the bottom of the strait in his deep-sea diving craft. In March, 1965, Cousteau reported that his explorations indicated it would be possible to build massive bridge piers on the strait floor. Many more years of study and planning will be needed before construction can begin. If a bridge does at last span the gulf between Scylla and Charybdis, its construction will be perhaps the most amazing engineering feat of an astonishing century of bridge-building progress.

Bibliography

AMMANN, OTHMAR H. "Brobdingnagian Bridges." *Smithsonian Institution Annual Report,* 1931.

BILLINGS, HENRY. *Bridges.* Viking Press, New York, 1956.

BLACK, ARCHIBALD. *The Story of Bridges.* McGraw-Hill, New York, 1936.

BOYER, DAVID S. "Over and Under Chesapeake Bay." *National Geographic Magazine,* April 1964.

FINCH, JAMES KIP. *The Story of Engineering.* Doubleday, New York, 1960.

GIES, JOSEPH. *Bridges and Men.* Doubleday, New York, 1963.

GRANT, MICHAEL. *The World of Rome.* World Publishing Company, Cleveland and New York, 1960. Paperback edition, Mentor Books, New York, 1961.

HOME, GORDON C. *Old London Bridge.* Dodd, Mead & Company, New York, 1931.

SINGER, CHARLES, and others, editors. *A History of Technology.* Volume I: *From Early Times to Fall of Ancient Empires.* Oxford University Press, New York and London, 1954.
Volume II: *The Mediterranean Civilizations and the Middle Ages c. 700 B.C. to A.D. 1500.* Oxford University Press, New York and London, 1956.
Volume III: *From the Renaissance to the Industrial Revolution c. 1500 to c. 1750.* Oxford University Press, New York and London, 1957.

Volume IV: *The Industrial Revolution c. 1750–1850.* Oxford University Press, New York and London, 1958.

Volume V: *The Late Nineteenth Century c. 1850 to c. 1900.* Oxford University Press, New York and London, 1958.

SMITH, H. SHIRLEY. *The World's Great Bridges.* Harper, New York, 1953.

STEINMAN, DAVID B. "Bridges." *Scientific American,* November 1954.

——— *The Builders of the Bridge.* Harcourt, Brace & Co., New York, 1945. Biography of John and Washington Roebling.

——— and Watson, Sara Ruth. *Bridges and their Builders.* Putnam, New York, 1941.

TALESE, GAY. *The Bridge.* Harper & Row, New York, 1964. About the construction of the Verrazano-Narrows Bridge.

WHEELER, HAROLD, editor. *Marvels of the Modern World.* Doubleday, Doran & Co., New York, 1941.

Index

Index

Abutment, definition of, 16
Adda River, 48
Aelius Bridge, 33
Alcántara, 34–35
Ambassador Bridge, 141
Ammann, Othmar Hermann, 104, 112–118, 121, 123, 132, 139–141,
    145, 149, 153–154, 161–162, 164, 167, 170–171
Apollodorus, 33
Aqueducts, 36–38
Arch bridges, 14, 16–17, 21, 24, 28, 59, 80, 92, 110
    wooden arch, 28–31, 34, 61
    stone arch, 30–31, 34–37, 41–57, 172
    iron arch, 56–60
    steel arch, 69–71, 75–78, 91, 100–105, 113, 155, 160
    concrete arch, 31, 106–107, 172
    hinged arch, 100–101
Arno River, 47–48
Australia, 104, 107
Avignon, 44–46

Babylon, 22–24
Babylonians, 21–24, 27

Baker, Benjamin, 95
Bay Bridge, *see* San Francisco-Oakland Bay Bridge
Bayonne Bridge, 103–105, 113, 121
Beam bridges (also known as girder bridges), 14–17, 23, 61, 91, 106, 172, *see also* Cantilever bridges
Bear Mountain Bridge, 110
Bends, *see* Caisson disease
Bénoît, 44–46
Bessemer, Henry, 70
Birchenough Bridge, 104
Bouch, Thomas, 92, 94–95, 148
Bronx-Whitestone Bridge, 119, 121, 140–141, 144, 147
Brooklyn Bridge, 17, 78–80, 84–90, 94, 96, 101, 109, 111, 115, 117, 139
Brown, Samuel, 59
Buchanan, James, 69
Buildwas Bridge, 58

Caesar, Julius, 30, 35–36, 40
Caisson disease (also known as "the bends"), 73–75, 86, 111
Caissons, description of, 71–72
Canada, 83, 98, 146
Cantilever bridges, 91–92, 95–100, 107, 110, 113, 118, 130, 136, 172
Capellen Bridge, 106
Carnegie, Andrew, 75
Cast iron, 56, 69–70
Chesapeake Bay, 154–157, 160
Chesapeake Bay Bridge-Tunnel, 154–161
Chesapeake Channel Tunnel, 157
China, 18, 29
Cincinnati Bridge, 83–84
Clam bridges, 15, *see also* Beam bridges
Clapper bridges, 15–16, *see also* Beam bridges
Claudius (Roman Emperor), 40
Coalbrookdale Bridge, 57–58
Cofferdam, description of, 32, 71–72
Colorado River, 109
Columbia River, 172
Compression, definition of, 17

Cooper, Theodore, 76–77, 98–100, 198
Cousteau, Jacques-Yves, 174

Danube Bridge, 33–34
Danube River, 33
Darby, Abraham, 57–58
Diodorus Siculus, 22–23

Eads, James Buchanan, 68–78, 80, 84–87, 91, 95, 98, 100–101, 112
East River, 79, 85–90, 96, 101, 111
Egypt, 21, 27
Eiffel, Gustave, 101
Eldridge, Clark, 142–143
Ellet, Charles, 81–82
England, 15, 40–44, 56–58, 60, 72, 173
Erie Canal, 110
Etruscans, 28–30
Euphrates River, 21–24, 32

Fabricius, Lucius, 31
Fairmount Bridge, 62–63
Finley, James, 59
Firth of Forth, 92, 94–96
Firth of Tay, 92, 94
Florence, 47–48
Forth Bridge, 94–96, 98, 100
Fowler, John, 95
France, 14, 36–37, 40, 44, 48–52, 55–56

Gaddi, Taddeo, 47
"Galloping Gertie," *see* Tacoma-Narrows Bridge
Gard River, 36
George Washington Bridge, 17, 90, 113–118, 121, 123, 132, 137, 139–141, 144, 161–162, 171
Gerber, Heinrich, 95
Germany, 31, 101, 172
Giocondo, Fra Giovanni, 49, 51
Girder bridges, *see* Beam bridges

Golden Gate Bridge, 17, 20, 90, 126–127, 132–137, 139–141, 144–147, 153, 161–162, 168·
Grand Canal, Venice, 52
Greeks, 25–27

Hadrian (Roman Emperor), 33
Hell Gate Bridge, 101–104, 113, 123, 141
Hellespont, 25
Henry Hudson Bridge, 104–105
Herodotus, 22–23, 25, 32
Holland Tunnel, 111
Home, Gordon, 41
Honeymoon Bridge, 101
Hooghly Bridge, 100
Horatius, 28–29
Hudson River, 109–118, 121, 132
Humber River Bridge, 173

Île de la Cité, 48–51
Italy, 27–28, 47–48, 52–54, 154, 174

Jaminet, Dr., 74–75, 87
Japan, 174
Jefferson, Thomas, 14
John Day Bridge, 172

Karman, Theodore von, 145
Keystone Bridge Company, 71
Kill van Kull, 104, 113
Kingston-Rhinecliff Bridge, 121
Kwan Hsien, 18

Lacer, Caius Julius, 34–35
Lake Washington, 172
Lincoln, Abraham, 69
Lincoln Tunnel, 112
Lindenthal, Gustav, 102, 112–113
Linville, J. H., 71
London, 40–44, 58, 107, 110

London Bridge, 40–45, 47, 58
Long Island Sound Bridge, 173

Mackinac Bridge, 148–149, 151–154, 161
Manhattan Bridge, 101, 141
Marcius, Ancus, 28
Melan, Joseph, 106
Menai Bridge, 58–60, 80
Menai Strait, 58
Merrimac, The, 69
Mesopotamia, 21–22, 24
Messina Straits Bridge, 154, 174–175
Mexico, 29
Michener, Percy, 156
Mid-Hudson Bridge, 110
Mississippi River, 67–69, 77, 79, 109
Moisseiff, Leon S., 141–142, 144, 146–148, 151
Monier, Joseph, 106
Monitor, The, 69

Nabopolassar, 23–24
Natural bridges, 14
Nebuchadnezzar, 23
Neuilly Bridge, 55
New York Bridge Company, 80
New York City, 79–81, 84–90, 101, 104, 109–118, 121–123, 125–126, 154, 161–170, 173
Niagara Bridge, 81–83
Niagara River, 81–82, 101
Nile River, 21
Nitocris, Queen, 22–23, 32
Normans, 40

Ohio River, 65

Palmer, Timothy, 62
Paris, 48–52, 55
Perronet, Jean, 55–56
Peru, 18

Peter of Colechurch, 41–42, 44–45
Pier, definition of, 15
Plauen Bridge, 31
Pons Fabricius, 31
Pons Sublicius, 28–29
Pont d'Arc, 14
Pont d'Avignon, 44–47
Pont du Gard, 36–38
Pont Neuf, 50–51
Pont Notre Dame, 48–49, 51
Ponte, Antonio da, 53–54
Ponte Sant' Angelo, *see* Aelius Bridge
Ponte Santa Trinità, 47–49
Ponte Vecchio, 47–48
Pontifex Maximus, 29
Pontoon bridges, 24–25, 118, 172
Port of New York Authority, 111–113, 116, 161
Portugal, 172
Pozzolana, 30
Pritchard, Thomas Farnolls, 56–57
Puget Sound, 140
Purcell, C. H., 127–128

Quebec Bridge, 98–100, 113, 136, 148
Queensboro Bridge, 96, 101, 113

Rainbow Bridge, 101
Recompression chamber, 75
Reinforced concrete, 105–106, 172
Rennie, John, 58
Rhine Bridge, 35
Rhine River, 35, 40
Rhodesia, 104
Rhône River, 44–45
Rialto Bridge, 52–54
Rip Van Winkle Bridge, 118
Rochester Bridge, 72
Rock Island Bridge, 68
Roebling, John, 80–84, 87–91, 112, 139, 161

Roebling, Washington, 83–90, 98, 112, 139, 161
Roman Empire, 27–38
Romans, 15, 17, 21, 27–41, 45, 47–48
Rome, 28, 33–34, 36, 39
Rope bridges, 18–21
Russian Gulch, 107

St. Lawrence River, 98–99
St. Louis and Illinois Bridge Company, 68, 71
St. Louis Bridge, 67–68, 70–78, 84–85, 95–96, 98, 100, 117
San Andreas Fault, 126
San Francisco, 123, 125–138
San Francisco Bay, 125–138
San Francisco-Oakland Bay Bridge, 127–132, 137, 140–141, 145
Sandö Bridge, 107
Sava River, 16
Scamozzi, 54
Schuylkill River, 62
Scotland, 59, 92–96
Segovia, Aqueduct of, 38
Seine River, 48–51, 55
Semiramis, Queen, 22–23
Severn River, 56–58
Spain, 34, 38
Spuyten Duyvil Creek, 104
Steel, 69–70, 172
Steinman, David, 113, 121, 141, 146–147, 149, 153–154, 174
Strait of Mackinac, 148, 151
Strauss, Joseph B., 127, 132–134, 139
Sumerians, 21, 24, 28, 30
Suspension bridges, 14, 17–21, 58–60, 80–90, 92, 95–97, 107, 109–110, 112–118, 121, 123, 126–130, 132–137, 139–154, 161–170, 172
Sweden, 107

Tacoma-Narrows Bridge, 140–149, 153
Tagus River, 34
Tappan Zee Bridge, 118
Tay Bridge, 92–95, 100, 148
Telford, Thomas, 57–60, 80

Tension, definition of, 17
Thames River, 40–42, 44–45, 58–59
Thimble Shoal Channel Tunnel, 157
Thousand Islands Bridge, 146–147
Throgs Neck Bridge, 120–121
Tiber River, 28–29, 33
Tibet, 18
Tigris River, 21, 24
Tokyo Bay Bridge, 174
Trajan (Roman Emperor), 33–35, 38
Triborough Bridge, 121, 141
Truss bridges, 61–64, 68, 91–94, 118, 121, 153, 172
    bowstring truss, 63–64
Tsao-chow Bridge, 118
Tweed Bridge, 59
Tweed River, 59

Ulloa, Don Antonio de, 18
Union Pacific Railroad, 68

Venice, 52–54
Verrazano, Giovanni da, 162–164
Verrazano-Narrows Bridge, 81, 90, 121, 137, 154, 161–170, 173–174
Vitruvius, 32
Voussoirs, definition of, 30

Wales, 58–60
Walt Whitman Bridge, 122–123
Washington Toll Bridge Authority, 142–143, 148
Waterloo Bridge, 107
Wheeling Bridge, 82
Whipple, Squire, 63–64
Wigram, E. T. A., 34
Wilkinson, John, 57
William the Conqueror, 40
Williamsburg Bridge, 96, 101, 140
Woodruff, Glenn, 145, 149, 153
Wrought iron, 56, 69–70

Xerxes, King of Persia, 25–26

Yellow River, 118
Yerba Buena Island, 128, 130
Yugoslavia, 16

THE AUTHOR

ROBERT SILVERBERG *is a native New Yorker and attended Columbia University. He began writing professionally when still an undergraduate, and his first book was published in 1955, a year before his graduation. He and his wife, who is an electronics engineer, live in the huge old house in the Riverdale section of New York that was formerly the home of Fiorello La Guardia.*

Editor of the anthology GREAT ADVENTURES IN ARCHAE-OLOGY, *Mr. Silverberg has written many books on scientific and archaeological subjects—among them* LOST CITIES AND VANISHED CIVILIZATIONS, EMPIRES IN THE DUST, THE GREAT DOCTORS, MAN BEFORE ADAM, *and* NIELS BOHR: THE MAN WHO MAPPED THE ATOM. *He has made several trips to Europe, has visited most parts of the United States, and spends several weeks each winter exploring coral reefs in the Caribbean. One of his greatest pleasures is reading, and he collects rare books on the subjects that especially interest him.*